It All Begins With GENESIS

STUDENT

1:1
answersingenesis
Petersburg, Kentucky, USA

It All Begins in Genesis

Student Book NIV/NAS

A Student Book should be purchased for each student, whether in the Christian school classroom or in the homeschool environment. In a classroom setting, always order one extra for the teacher so that you have copies of everything for reference. Students will take home the pages of the Student Book throughout the study.

First printing: Janurary 2010

ISBN: 1-60092-297-X

Author: Sheila Richardson

Cover desgin and interior layout: Diane King

Scripture taken from the HOLY BIBLE, NEW INTERNATIONAL VERSION®. Copyright © 1973, 1978, 1984 International Bible Society. Used by permission of Zondervan. All rights reserved.

The "NIV" and "New International Version" trademarks are registered in the United States Patent and Trademark Office by International Bible Society. Use of either trademark requires the permission of International Bible Society.

Cover image © istockphoto.com/Aldo Murillo

Clipart © 2009 Jupiterimages Corporation. Used under license.

Printed in China

www.answersingenesis.org

Table of Contents

It All Begins With Genesis

There is more than one way to look at your world

When people look at the same event or object, they often think very different things. It's as if everyone wears different eyeglasses, and therefore each has a different view of what is really there.

For example, when you look at a beautiful cake, you may have different ideas about that cake, depending on what you know about cake or the maker of the cake.

Mary made this cake.
Mary bought the cake.

Cake tastes good.
Cake is too sweet.

Cake is good for you.
Cake is bad for you.

This is a beautiful cake.
This is a 'tacky' cake.

When people think about God, they have different ideas, too.

There is a God who is all-powerful, all-knowing, eternal and ever-present.
There is no God.
Everything is God. All is divine.

When people look at the world, what different ideas do they have?

God created the world.

The world evolved by chance.

When people look at themselves, what different ideas do they have?

Mankind is just a cosmic accident.   Man came up from the slime.
Man was created in the image of God.   There is no purpose for man's life.
Man has a special purpose.   Why bother?

In the coming weeks, we are going to be talking a lot about something called a WORLDVIEW. And we are going to learn, through the study of the book of beginnings, Genesis, what a CHRISTIAN WORLDVIEW really is.

1. We will begin with the word 'worldview' and see what it means. Your teacher will be giving you a word puzzle to unscramble. Take the words in your puzzle and paste them in the right order below. This should give you a good definition of worldview.

2. Here are some other ideas that help us to understand worldview:

    •   A worldview is what you believe about the world because of what you believe about God.

    •   A worldview is the 'big picture' of life. It starts with an understanding of God, which then helps you to fit together all the individual pieces of your world.

3. Your worldview gives you the answers to the really important, difficult questions of life. It begins with questions such as these:

    Who is God?   **What has He done?**   **What can He do?**
    What is God like?   **Can I really trust Him?**

    The way you answer those important questions will then give you answers to other questions, such as these:

    Who am I?   **What is my purpose in life?**
    What is really true? **Why do bad things happen?**

    Finally, all the answers will come together as you answer the key question:

    How then should I live?

4. We know that people have many different ways of looking at their world.

    Where do you suppose people get their ideas about the world? Write your thoughts below, or discuss them with your class.

    _____

    _____

    _____

    _____

5. When people have different ideas about something, such as who made the cake in the example we saw, what is the best way to discover what is really true? Which of the following is the best way to 'settle the matter'? Put a check ✓ beside your answer.

    _____ Ask your best friend what he thinks.

    _____ Ask your teacher at school.

    _____ Look in the newspaper.

    _____ Ask the eyewitness who was there when the cake was made or bought.

6. When it comes to questions about who God is, what He is like, who made the world, who made you or why were you made, was there an eyewitness? Who?

    _____

7. Do we have that eyewitness report written down anywhere? Where?

    _____

8. Finally, considering your answer to the last question, where should we look to find truth that will give us the answers to all those hard worldview questions?

    _____

9. Can you trust what you read in the Bible? What does the Bible say about itself? Read the passages below and *highlight* or *underline* what you learn about what is true.

2 Timothy 3:16–17 (NIV) 'All Scripture is God-breathed and is useful for teaching, rebuking, correcting and training in righteousness, so that the man of God may be thoroughly equipped for every good work.'

Psalm 119:142 (NIV) 'Your righteousness is everlasting and your law [meaning God's Word] is true.'

John 1:14 (NIV) 'The Word became flesh and made his dwelling among us. We have seen his glory, the glory of the one and only, who came from the Father, full of grace and truth.'

John 14:6 (NIV) 'Jesus answered, "I am the way and the truth and the life. No one comes to the Father except through me." '

John 17:17 (NIV) 'Sanctify [means 'make holy' or 'set aside for His use'] them by the truth; your word is truth.'

10. Let's think a little more about how Scripture can give us truth—a worldview that really gives us the answers that will 'work' in our lives.

For example, consider these questions:

   How did the world get here? How did I get here?

Read the Scriptures below and *underline* or *highlight* what the eyewitness (the Creator) tells us about how the heavens, the Earth and all living things came to be.

Genesis 1:1 (NIV) 'In the beginning God created the heavens and the earth.'

Genesis 1:26–27 (NIV) 'Then God said, "Let us make man in our image, in our likeness, and let them rule over the fish of the sea and the birds of the air, over the livestock, over all the earth, and over all the creatures that move along the ground." So God created man in his own image, in the image of God he created him; male and female he created them.'

Psalm 148:5 (NIV) 'Let them [the angels, sun, moon, stars, highest heavens, waters above the heavens] praise the name of the LORD, for he commanded and they were created.'

Isaiah 40:26 (NIV) 'Lift your eyes and look to the heavens: Who created all these? He who brings out the starry host one by one, and calls them each by name.'

Isaiah 45:12 (NIV) 'It is I who made the earth and created mankind upon it. My own hands stretched out the heavens; I marshaled their starry hosts.'

Colossians 1:16 (NIV) 'For by him all things were created: things in heaven and on earth, visible and invisible, whether thrones or powers or rulers or authorities; all things were created by him and for him.'

11. Finally, before we stop for the week, we need to think about just one more question. Does it make a difference whether you are a special creation of God or you simply 'came from the slime'? Would it make any difference in your worldview? Would it make any difference how you would live? Think about it a moment and then write the answer below or discuss it in class.

_____

_____

_____

_____

Thanks for 'hanging in' this week with some new ideas and new '50-cent' words. You have made a good beginning. See you next week.

7 C's Connection: _____

The foundation for your worldview is Genesis

We are so glad that you will be studying Genesis with us. This could be one of the most important studies you have ever done!

We say this for two reasons.

The first reason is that the Book of Genesis is the foundation of our Bible. It is also the foundation of our worldview, which we talked about last week. All of the important teachings in our Bible have their beginning in the Book of Genesis. This wonderful book answers some of the most important questions you'll ever have: questions such as 'Who is God?' 'Who am I?' and 'Why am I here in this world?'

The second reason is that in this study we are not only going to teach you about Genesis, but we are going to teach you how to study the Bible for yourself—something we call 'inductive study.' You will learn something that many adults don't even know! You will learn to mine the treasures God gave us in His Word so that they will help you your whole life.

God's Word

God's World

In the coming weeks you will not only learn about God's Word, but you will learn about God's world. You will see how much fun it is to learn about the things God made. So, let's get started!

1. Look in your Bible and see where the Book of Genesis is found. What book comes before it?

    _____

    What book comes after it? _____

    Okay, so that was a trick question! Genesis comes first, and even its name means 'beginnings.'

2. The Book of Genesis is the foundation of the Bible. Consider for a moment what a foundation does for a house. What happens when the foundation is removed from under a house?

   _____

3. In your Bible, Psalm 11:3 talks about foundations. The verse is printed for you below. Read the verse and then write what would happen if the foundation of Genesis were destroyed. Can you think what might happen to the rest of the Bible if Genesis were destroyed? Give it some thought, and we'll discuss it in more detail later.

   Psalm 11:3 (NIV) 'When the foundations are being destroyed, what can the righteous do?'

   _____

4. The first step we take when we start to study a book of the Bible is something we call an 'overview.' The overview is a 'flying over' something. It is like being 5,000 feet in the air in a helicopter and looking at the ground below. This gives you the 'big picture.'

   Today we will look at the big picture of the first eleven chapters of Genesis. That is the part of Genesis that talks most about the origin (beginning) of things.

5. The first eleven chapters of Genesis talk about four major events in human history. Read the verses listed below. You will find Genesis 1–11 written out for you in the back of this workbook. Think about what event each is describing and write it down in the designated place on the overview chart on the next page. Beside each event, it might be helpful if you draw a picture that represents the events described.

   ✓ Genesis 1:1; 1:27–31; Genesis 2:8, 18

   ✓ Genesis 3:1, 6, 14–19; Genesis 4:8; Genesis 5:5, 8, 11, 14 (Look for just one repeated phrase.)

   ✓ Genesis 6:13–14; Genesis 7:11–12, 21–23

   ✓ Genesis 10:1; Genesis 11:1–9

Overview of Genesis 1–11

Chapter	Major events	Picture of events
1 and 2	creation	
3, 4, 5	fall	
6, 7, 8, 9	flood	
10, 11	nations	

6. Now that you have looked at the main events in the first eleven chapters of Genesis, let's consider again the question about the foundations being destroyed. (These are difficult thinking questions. Let's see what you can do with them.)

    ✓ Chapters 1 and 2 describe the creation of all things, the establishment of marriage and man's work on the earth. Discuss with your group or write below what problems would come to believers ('the righteous') if they did not have that foundation to live by.

    _____

    _____

    _____

    ✓ In chapters 3–5 we see the events surrounding the Fall of mankind through Adam and Eve, and the results of that Fall (sin and death). If we didn't know about the Fall of man, how would we understand where death and evil came from?

    ✓ In chapters 6–9 we see the judgment of the Flood in the days of Noah. Can you think how things would be different if believers didn't know about the Flood?

    ✓ In chapters 10–11 we see the descendants of Shem, Ham and Japheth; another judgment at Babel; and the origin of languages and nations. If believers didn't know these things, how different might things be?

You've done a great job of getting started in building your foundation in Genesis. You had a helicopter ride in order to see the big picture.

The overview is a bit like a 'preview of coming attractions.' We'll be studying much more about all these things in the weeks to come.

During the week, practice remembering the four major events of Genesis and in what chapters they are found.

7 C's Connection: _____

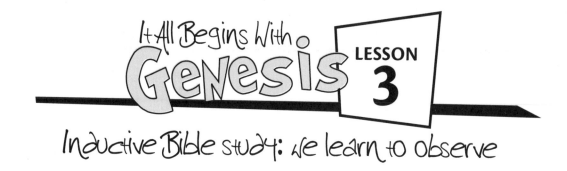

Inductive Bible study: We learn to observe

Inductive Bible study—that's a new expression for most of you. What is it, anyway? What's so special about it? This week you'll learn something about 'inductive study,' and you'll begin to observe more closely the foundation of a Biblical worldview—Genesis—using inductive principles.

1. Inductive Bible study (our new 50-cent word) is the type of Bible study in which the Bible is the PRIMARY SOURCE.

   What in the world does that mean?

   Primary means 'first.' So the Bible is the *first* place you go when you begin your study. You don't go to books about the Bible, you don't go to messages from your teacher or pastor, and you don't go to videos or comics. You go first to the Bible to see what it says.

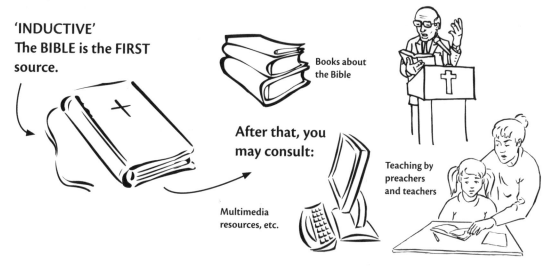

'INDUCTIVE'
The BIBLE is the FIRST source.

Books about the Bible

After that, you may consult:

Teaching by preachers and teachers

Multimedia resources, etc.

2. Why is it good to go first to the 'source'? Answer the following:

   ✓ If you really want to learn all you can learn about a certain girl at school, what would be the best way to do it? (circle)

   Ask her parents about her.

   Survey all the kids at school and ask them.

   See what her name means in the dictionary.

   Spend a lot of time with her and ask her questions.

✓ If you want to study frogs, what would be the most effective way to do so?

Ask your friend what he knows about frogs.

Read a book about frogs.

**Spend time with frogs. Observe them in their natural
 habitat, and then dissect one.**

Go to a frog lecture.

✓ If you really want to know God, to understand what He is like, what He has done
and how He wants you to live, what is the best way to do this?

Read books in which people tell you what they know about God.

Spend time in the Word of God, in which He tells you all about Himself.

Ask your Sunday school teacher.

Watch a religious TV channel.

3. It is a very good thing to read books about the Bible and to ask godly teachers to
teach you. But there are reasons why it is *best* to go first to the Bible itself and study it
yourself. Can you think of any of the reasons why this is good? Write them below and
we'll discuss this question in class.

_____

_____

_____

_____

_____

_____

3

4. Inductive Bible study has three parts, or components. Read the explanation below and discuss this with your teacher.

    When you study the Bible inductively, you learn to do three things every time you look at a passage of Scripture:

    a) First you ask, 'What does this passage *say*?' (OBSERVATION)

    b.) You then ask, 'What does it *mean*?' (INTERPRETATION)

    c.) Finally, it is important to let the meaning of the text be used by the Lord to change your life. You ask, 'How am I now to live?' 'How do I walk?' 'What is there in this passage that needs to become a part of me?' (APPLICATION)

5. The most important skill to learn in inductive Bible study is *observation*. We need to observe carefully, because that will determine how we interpret and then how we apply what we learn.

    We observe by asking questions.

    We bet you're pretty good at asking questions already ... all kinds of questions: 'Who really likes me?' 'Where am I going this Saturday?' 'Why do I have to do my math homework?' 'When is it going to be time for dinner?' 'How can I get better grades?'

6. Learning to use the 'Five W's and an H' is like playing the game of Jeopardy. You are given the answer, and your job is to come up with the question it is answering. Let's practice a little with some different verses in Scripture. We'll give you the verse, and you write the question that is being answered. (Sometimes the verse will tell you a 'who,' other times it will tell you a 'why' and sometimes it will answer more than one question.)

The Six Questions—the six 'magic words' of inductive Bible study

Who?   **What?**

Where?   **When?**

Why?   **How?**

✓ **Genesis 1:1** (NAS) 'In the beginning, God created the heavens and the earth.'

_____

✓ **Genesis 2:8** (NAS) 'And the Lord God planted a garden toward the east, in Eden.'

_____

✓ **Genesis 3:10** (NAS) 'I was afraid because I was naked; so I hid myself.'

_____

7. When we study a book of the Bible inductively, there are certain steps we follow. You actually began STEP ONE last week when you looked at the different events found in the first eleven chapters of Genesis. You looked at Genesis from a helicopter view.

Can you remember what that 'helicopter view' is called? Write the word below:

_____

This first step of the inductive process gives you the 'big picture.' You ask questions from 5,000 feet, so you don't see many details. But you are able to form the framework that will make all those details easier to understand later. Later you will park that helicopter and get closer to what you are studying. You'll see more details then.

8. We are now ready to begin STEP TWO of the inductive study process. You have parked the helicopter. Now it is time for you to begin hiking.

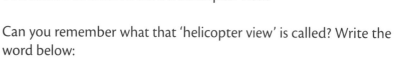

You are now going to cover the same territory that you covered when you flew over in a helicopter. But you will go more slowly and on ground level, so you will see things differently. You will spot things you missed when you were 5,000 feet in the air.

The same is true in your Bible study. You flew very quickly over the first eleven chapters of Genesis. You missed a lot! Now it is time to slow down and make your observations from 'ground level.' We'll begin with chapter 1.

9. At the end of this workbook you will find something we call 'observation sheets.' These are simply pages that have the text of the Scripture written down for you. You will be learning how to mark key words by using symbols and colors so that you will improve your observation skills.

10. We will introduce you to observation sheets today, and you will work with them in much more detail in weeks to come.

   Please take out your observation sheet for Genesis 1. In the margins you will see some questions to answer. Follow the directions given there.

We've covered a lot this week!

> *What* **is the definition of 'inductive study'?**
> *What* **three things do you do when you study a passage inductively?**
> *What* **are the 'six magic questions'?**
> *What* **are the first two steps of inductive study: helicopter view (overview)**
> **hiking (chapter study)**

Are you dizzy? Confused? Hang in there—you'll be amazed at how much you can learn about God and His Word once you begin to use inductive techniques.

7 C's Connection: _____

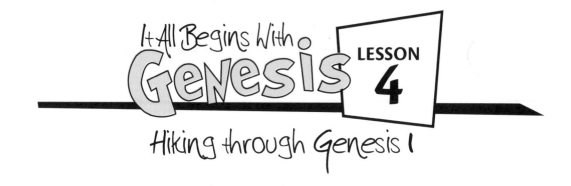

Hiking through Genesis 1

You have parked your helicopter (the overview), and you will be continuing the hike (chapter study) through Genesis 1. You began this hike last week.

What an awesome chapter of the Bible!

In it you will learn about the Creator by looking at what He has made and how He made it.

You will be better able to answer the worldview question 'Who is God?'

1. Take out the observation sheet for Genesis 1 that you started last week. You began by answering a few 'who' and 'what' questions from the chapter. Today we will continue to question the chapter for more of the details God gives us. (Please read all the instructions that follow before you begin your work on the observation sheet.)

2. KEY WORDS = keys to understanding Scripture. When we study Scripture, we always look for key words and phrases. A word is called a 'key word' if it is a *repeated* word. In chapter 1, you already saw that the word 'God' is repeated many times, so it is a key word. Key phrases are when two or three words together are used over and over, such as 'it was good.'

   ✓ When you see a key word, you should mark it. You can use colored pencils, pens or highlighters. For example, 'God' is a key word in this chapter. You have already marked this. You also marked 'man.' We suggested how to mark the word, but you can choose how you like to mark all your own key words. You could

      color it one color (like red or purple), or

      draw a box around the word and fill it in with a different color, or

      mark it by drawing a symbol on it or around it.

   ✓ When you mark or color a key word, you also mark or color other forms of the same word. For example, since 'God' is a key word, mark or color all words that talk about God, such as 'Lord,' 'Lord God' or 'Father,' the same way you marked or colored 'God,' because they go together.

✓ When you mark or color a key word, you also mark or color the pronouns of the same key word. For example, when you mark God, you also mark 'He,' 'His,' 'my,' 'mine,' when they refer to God.

3. Now that you have finished reading the instructions, turn to your observation sheet from the last lesson and check to see if you have marked God and man, with all their pronouns and synonyms (words that mean the same thing).

4. Are you finished? Let's try another word. One of the words God repeats over and over in Genesis 1 is the word 'said.' Read through Genesis 1 again, and this time put a red box around every mention of 'said.' Count how many times the word 'said' appears:

_____

5. Since God repeats that word so much, it must be important. In Scripture we often read about God's 'Word,' His 'speaking,' His 'saying,' His 'commanding.' This is a very important key word. Below you will find an important verse that talks about the Lord's speaking or saying. The verse is Hebrew poetry. Highlight or underline in a color what happens in the verse when the Lord spoke:

Psalm 33:6 (NIV) 'By the word of the LORD were the heavens made, their starry host by the breath of his mouth.'

 6. In addition to the word 'said,' have you noticed that there are a lot of other 'action words' (verbs) which describe what God did in chapter 1? Your next assignment for the day will be to go through chapter 1 again and make a black box around each of the other action words.

created	**made**	**saw**	**called**
placed	**separated**	**blessed**	

Remember, the purpose here is not merely to mark a lot of words and have a colorful paper! The purpose is to see what we can learn about God by what He did in creation. Every key word marked should tell you something more about the God of creation.

7. Now you have something else 'key' to mark. We need to see some key phrases in Genesis 1. Phrases include more than one word. Genesis is full of key phrases. Today we want you to mark the following:

    'It was good.' (Make brackets around the phrase in blue, like this: <it was good>)

    'It was so.' (Make orange brackets around this phrase.)

    'After their [or its] kind.' (Make green brackets around this phrase.)

    What do these phrases, repeated over and over again, tell you about the God of creation?

8. When you see all that God says and does in chapter 1, what does that tell you about this God? Even if you never heard about Him before, what might you say He was like after you see all He has made? Pretend you are explaining this to someone who has never heard about God. Tell your classmates.

Wow, what an awesome God! Do you ever spend time just looking at God's creation and thinking about the One who made all these things? The activity below helps you do just that. If you have a clear night tonight, see what you can learn from doing this activity.

Activity: God's creation of the universe

Choose a clear night this week, and go outside to a place where there are not many lights, and spend five or ten minutes being quiet and looking at the universe above you. What different things do you observe? What kind of thoughts do you have? What do you learn about the God who made all this? Discuss this with your parents or with your class.

7 C's Connection: _____

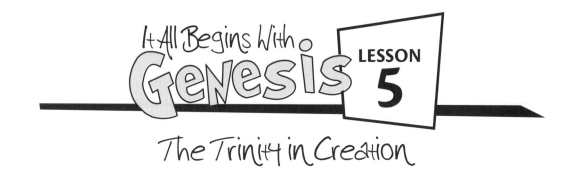

The Trinity in Creation

Who is God? What is He like? These are two questions people ask as they form their worldview. We'll find some more answers to these questions as we continue our inductive study of Genesis 1 this week.

But first, we have more to learn about inductive Bible study.

1. **Review time!** You have been learning some principles of inductive study. Let's see how much you remember about some of the things we have introduced. Below there are some pictures we used to illustrate some of the important things we hope you are learning. All you have are the pictures, no explanation! Give it a try. In the space beside the picture, write what you remember the picture is supposed to teach you.

   ✓ Inductive study

   ✓ The 'six magic words' of inductive study

   ✓ Step 1 of inductive study

   ✓ Step 2 of inductive study

   ✓

How did you do? Don't worry—just as God repeats the things that are important, we'll be repeating them again and again until you've 'got it.'

2. **Step 3: stop and smell the roses.**

   You have learned that step 1 is the overview—you see the big picture from the helicopter. In step 2 you park the helicopter and begin your hike by marking key words and asking the magic questions of who, what, where, when, why and how. Now it's time for step 3.

Picture yourself hiking along a mountain path. Suddenly you see a beautiful wildflower. You don't know what it is, and you want to learn more about the flower. Next, you see a rock with minerals that glisten in the sunshine. What kind of rock is it? Well, you need to do more than just ask who, what, where, when, why and how. You need to bring out your field guides, which picture and identify rocks and flowers.

In other words, you need to look even closer.

How does this example apply to Bible study?

Word studies

Step 3 occurs when we study the Greek and Hebrew words. As you know, the original Scriptures were not written in English. The Old Testament was written in Hebrew and the New Testament in Greek. Sometimes, the translations into English seem confusing. You can read five different English-language Bibles and get different things. Often you can help the situation by studying the word in its original language.

No, you don't have to learn Greek and Hebrew in this course.

But sometimes we will give you information about a word that is particularly interesting or perhaps particularly confusing.

God in Genesis 1:1

Did you know that when the Book of Genesis was first written, it was written in the Hebrew language? When we look at the Hebrew name used for God in Genesis 1, we see it is the word '*Elohim*.' There are many different Hebrew names for God used in Scripture, each telling us something about His character, or who He is. The word *Elohim* is used whenever God's power is being shown. It was *Elohim* who was able to bring the universe into existence.

3. There is something else that is 'special' about the word *Elohim* in Genesis 1:1. It is a *plural* word, which means 'more than one.' Some scholars believe that the use of the plural in Genesis 1 shows us that the entire Trinity was involved in Creation.

4. Do you know what the Trinity is? The Word of God teaches us that God is One, but He is made up of three Persons. Pretty strange, isn't it? It is a mystery to us just how this all works, but we are told there is God the Father, God the Son and God the Holy Spirit. They are three, and they are each fully God.

    So, when you see the plural *Elohim* in Genesis 1:1, what does that tell you about who created the heavens and the earth? Write what you think below.

    _____

    _____

5. Genesis not only tells us that the entire Trinity was involved in Creation, but in the Word of God we learn more about what each member of the Godhead was doing. You have a chance now to practice your who, what, where, when, why and how skills as we look at some verses about the Trinity in Creation.

6. What do you think was the job of God the Holy Spirit in Creation? Read Genesis 1:2 below. It answers some of our 'Five W's and H' questions.

    Genesis 1: 2 (NIV) 'Now the earth was formless and empty, darkness was over the surface of the deep, and the Spirit of God was hovering over the waters.'

    ✓ Who is being talked about here?

    _____

    ✓ What was the condition of the earth when the Spirit was mentioned?

    _____

    ✓ What did the Spirit of God do?

    _____

7. Let's think a minute about what was happening in the verse above. (Let's see how you do at a little physics!) It was the beginning of creation, right? And the earth was not formed yet; it was just formless matter. And it was dark.

   What did the Spirit do over the surface? _____ The Hebrew word for 'hovered' is *rahap*, and it means 'flutter' or 'vibrate.'

   Vibration is energy, and energy was necessary in order to have form in the creation. The vibration of the Holy Spirit might be understood as the introduction of energy into the initially forceless creation.

   Look at Genesis 1:3, and write what happened after the Spirit began His 'vibrating.'

   _____

8. Now we are going outside the Book of Genesis to learn more about the role of the Trinity in Creation. Was the Son of God present at Creation? What was He doing? Read the passage below and answer the 'Five W's and H' questions you find there:

   Colossians 1:15–16 (NIV) 'He [Jesus] is the image of the invisible God, the firstborn over all creation. For by him all things were created: things in heaven and on earth, visible and invisible, whether thrones or powers or rulers or authorities; all things were created by him and for him.'

   ✓ Who does this verse tell you Jesus is? (two things)

   _____

   _____

   ✓ What did Jesus do?

   _____

   _____

   ✓ Why did He do it?

   _____

9. What was God the Father's role in Creation? Read the cross-reference from the Book of Hebrews below. It answers many questions about God, but you only need to answer the ones asked below.

    Hebrews 1:1–2 (NIV) 'In the past God spoke to our forefathers through the prophets at many times and in various ways, but in these last days he has spoken to us by his Son, whom he appointed heir of all things, and through whom he made the universe.'

    ✓ How did God speak to us 'in these last days'?

    _____

    ✓ What did God appoint His Son to be?

    _____

    ✓ How did God make the universe?

    _____

    Hebrews 11:3 (NIV) 'By faith we understand that the universe was formed at God's command, so that what is seen was not made out of what was visible.'

    ✓ How was the universe formed?

    _____

    ✓ What were the things that are seen *not* made out of?

    _____

    ✓ How can we understand these things?

    _____

10. **Our last step of inductive study**

Do you remember the first three steps of inductive study? Write them below:

1. _____

2. _____

3. _____

You were actually doing **step 4 of inductive study** when you looked at the verses in Colossians and Hebrews. You haven't been looking at Genesis. Instead, you have been looking at other Scriptures that tell you more about the things you are learning in Genesis.

This step is what we call the 'satellite view.' Remember, you have already flown over at 5,000 feet where you got a big-picture view. Then you looked at more detail in the hiking and 'smelling the roses' view. Now you need an even bigger view. You need to see the whole continent, not just a little view from 5,000 feet.

When you do Bible study, this step is called 'cross-referencing.' You were looking at cross-references when you looked at the passages in Colossians and Hebrews.

This means that you want to see what the *whole* Bible has to say about a subject talked about in the book you are studying. We will be looking at lots of cross-references throughout the Bible that help us to better understand Genesis.

11. Now it is time to go back to the observation worksheet for Genesis 1 that you have been working on. It's time to continue the 'hike.'

Mark each of the following key phrases in a distinctive way: 'one day,' 'a second day,' 'a third day,' 'a fourth day,' 'a fifth day,' 'the sixth day.' [Suggestion: circle each word in blue.]

12. With those markings as your guide, write in the chart on the next page what God created on each day. Do not copy the verses word by word; just read the verses and list one by one what God created on that day. It will help you to learn better to see it all in chart form.

The Days of Creation

Day 1 (verses 1–5)

Day 4 (verses 14–19)

Day 2 (verses 6–8)

Day 5 (verses 20–23)

Day 3 (verse 9–13)

Day 6 (verse 24–27)

7 C's Connection: _____

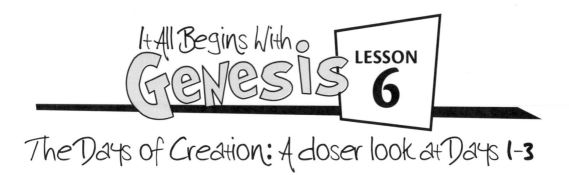

The Days of Creation: A closer look at Days 1-3

Can you imagine what it would have been like to be there when God created the world and brought everything into existence? Close your eyes for a minute and picture it in your mind!

This week we're going to see step by step in our minds what God says in His Word, and we're going to learn some wonderful things about His world. You will have a chance to do a lot of drawing, so get your colored pencils, pens or crayons ready!

Day 1 of Creation

1. **Genesis 1:2** (NAS) says, 'And the earth was formless and void, and darkness was over the surface of the deep; and the Spirit of God was moving over the surface of the waters.'

   When the Bible says that the earth was 'formless,' it means that it had no shape yet.

   When the Bible says that the earth was 'void,' it means it was empty, or vacant.

   Energy is what must happen to fill the 'void,' and to shape the matter that had no form yet. When we read Genesis 1:2, we see that 'the Spirit of God was moving over the surface of the waters.' The Hebrew word for moving (Hebrew—*rahap*) actually means 'to flutter, to shake, to vibrate.' Write on the line below where you think energy came from, according to Genesis 1:2. (Do you remember this from the last lesson?)

   _____

We see as we read on in Genesis 1 that God used energy to create light, dry land, life and all the other things. In fact, only God can make something out of nothing. It is He who made the complete, beautiful world we see today.

2. Think about what you've learned. In the space given at the right, draw how you think the earth looked when it was 'formless and void.'

    'And the earth was formless and void, and darkness was over the surface of the deep' (Genesis 1:2a, NAS).

3. Now draw how you think the earth looked as 'the Spirit of God was moving over the surface of the waters.'

    'And the Spirit of God was moving over the surface of the waters' (Genesis 1:2b, NAS).

4. Read Genesis 1:3–5. In the spaces at the right, draw what happened.

    'Then God said, "Let there be light" ' (Genesis 1:3, NAS).

    'And God saw that the light was good; and God separated the light from the darkness. And God called the light "day," and the darkness he called "night" … . Evening and morning—one day' (Genesis 1:4–5, NAS).

Day 2 of Creation

As Day 1 of Creation ends, we find that the Spirit was bringing energy to what was unorganized matter, and light followed. How exciting that the 'Light of the world' brought light. But what comes next?

5. **Genesis 1:6** (NAS) says: 'Let there be an expanse in the midst of the waters, and let it separate the waters from the waters.' Before you can draw it, you need to look closely at what the word 'expanse' is really telling you.

   ✓ The Hebrew word for 'expanse' is *raqia*. It means 'a spreading out or stretching out.'

   ✓ To understand the expanse better, read Genesis 1:7–8. (You can use your observation sheet for chapter 1.) What did God call the expanse?

   _____

   ✓ Now read Genesis 1:16–17. What does God place in the expanse on Day 4 of the Creation Week?

   _____

   ✓ You can learn even more about what is meant by 'expanse' by reading Genesis 1:20. These events happened on Day 4 of Creation Week and tell you what else is found in the expanse.

   _____

✓ Genesis 1:6 tells us that God took the waters and put some above the expanse and some below the expanse. Pretty interesting! Where do you think the 'waters above' are located today? In the space below, draw what you think Genesis 1:7–8 looked like. (Remember, God hasn't put the birds, stars and moon there yet.)

'And God made the expanse, and separated the waters which were below the expanse from the waters which were above the expanse; and it was so. And God called the expanse heaven' (Genesis 1:7–8a, NAS).

Day 3 of Creation

6. In the space given, draw what this verse describes:

'Then God said, "Let the waters below the heavens be gathered into one place, and let the dry land appear" and it was so. And God called the dry land earth, and the gathering of the waters He called seas' (Genesis 1:9–10a, NAS).

7. Draw how you think it looked in Genesis 1:12.

'And the earth brought forth vegetation, plants yielding seed after their kind and trees bearing fruit with seed in them after their kind, and God saw that it was good' (Genesis 1:12, NAS).

(Notice that when God created trees, they already had seed and fruit on them. They didn't start with a little seed that grew and developed; they were already producing fruit.)

Activity: learn about God from the leaves

If there are leaves on the trees, go for a walk and collect as many different kinds of leaves as you can find. Remember, God created them 'after their kind.' Spread them out and look at them and answer the following questions:

How many different kinds of leaves did you find?_____

What did you observe from the leaves that helped you understand more about our Creator?

Or learn about God from the wildflowers

If the season of the year is right, go out into the fields and see how many different kinds of wild flowers and/or garden flowers you can collect (with permission). Count how many different kinds of flowers you found. What did you observe about the flowers that helped you understand more about our Creator?

7 C's Connection: _____

The Days of Creation: A closer look at Days 4-6

Day 4 of Creation

1. Read Genesis 1:14–19. You may use your observation sheet. Read carefully!

2. What did God create on Day 4?

   _____

3. Look at verses 14–15 and list the six purposes of the lights.

   a. _____   d. _____

   b. _____   e. _____

   c. _____   f. _____

4. Now let's go to a cross-reference. **Psalm 19:1** (NAS) tells us:

   'The heavens are telling of the glory of God; and the firmament [their expanse] is declaring the work of His hands.'

   Does this verse tell you anything about *why* God created the universe? Write below what the heavens show you.

   _____

   _____

5. The next few questions are tough, and you'll have to think about them a little. On what day was light created?

   _____

6. Since the sun, moon and stars weren't created until the *fourth* day, we know that the original light did *not* come from

   _____

7. How would you explain the light that came before the sun, moon and stars? There are some good 'hints' from Scripture.

    ✓ Read **Psalm 104:1–3a** (NIV) below. This is poetry, and it says things in picture language. But it still is true. It sounds a lot like Day 1 of Creation, doesn't it?

    'Praise the LORD, O my soul. O LORD my God, you are very great; you are clothed with splendor and majesty. He wraps himself in light as with a garment; he stretches out the heavens like a tent and lays the beams of his upper chambers on their waters.'

    What does this passage tell you about the light at Creation? Does it say the sun was responsible for the light? Where then did the light come from?

    _____

    ✓ Now read these passages that tell us about Heaven.

    Revelation 21:23 (NIV) 'The city does not need the sun or the moon to shine on it, for the glory of God gives it light, and the Lamb is its lamp.'

    Revelation 22:5 (NIV) 'There will be no more night. They will not need the light of a lamp or the light of the sun, for the Lord God will give them light. And they will reign forever and ever.'

    According to this passage, where will the light come from in Heaven? Do they need a sun in Heaven?

    _____

    ✓ Finally, how would you answer someone who tells you that Genesis couldn't be true, because the light came before the sun and you must have a sun to have light?

    _____

    _____

    Did you know that ancient people wanted to worship the sun? Even today people worship the stars in the astrology charts. Do you suppose that God *knew* His people would want to worship the sun and stars, and He showed those who would look at His Word that *He* was the source of all light, not the sun? He is the One who should be worshipped.

8. **Psalm 147:4** (NAS) tells us something pretty amazing.

   'He counts the number of the stars; He gives names to all of them.'

   Write below what God knows about the stars. Why is that so amazing?

   _____

   _____

   If God knows that much about the stars He created, what do you think He knows about you?

9. In the space provided, draw how you think it looked when God created the lights.

   'And God made the two great lights, the greater light to govern the day, and the lesser light to govern the night; He made the stars also. And God placed them in the expanse of the heavens to give light on the earth' (Genesis 1:16–17, NAS).

All about eyeglasses

10. Before we go on to study Day 5 of Creation, we need to pause a moment and review something we talked about in the first lesson. We talked about worldviews—how everyone looks at the same world, but comes up with very different ideas about it.

    See if you can remember what a worldview is, and write it below. (If you forgot, go back to lesson 1 and see the definition you pasted on the page.)

    _____

    _____

Everyone looks at the same flower, but they look through different eyeglasses (their worldview). One person may have magnifying eyeglasses, and things look larger than they are. Others view through colored lenses, and that makes things different. Others have very wavy glass, so what they see is distorted.

As we study the beginning of things (their origin), we are going to study two major worldviews, two very different ways of viewing the universe and living things. There are other worldviews about origins, but these are the two we see most often.

The two kinds of eyeglasses (worldviews) we will study:

Naturalistic eyeglasses

The person who views the world through these eyeglasses believes that everything there is came about through chance and by the natural processes we observe operating throughout time. This person would not believe that divine intervention was required in creation.

Biblical eyeglasses

The person who views the world through these eyeglasses believes that there was an eyewitness to creation: God Himself. God tells us about the origin of things in His Word, and His Word is true. We are able to see plan, purpose and intelligent design in all that is.

Day 5 of Creation

11. Read **Genesis 1:20–21.** (You can use your observation sheet.) List below what God created on Day 5.

_____

_____

12. 'After their kind'—this phrase is repeated often in Genesis 1, isn't it? It *must* be important! (Would you call it a 'key phrase'?) Count how many times God uses the expression 'after their kind' in Genesis 1. Record the number here:

_____

What do you suppose God is trying to tell us about the way He created?

13. There are two different ways people look at the creation of living things. Do you remember the eyeglasses? There are some who look at the world with naturalistic eyeglasses. The other eyeglasses are the biblical eyeglasses.

First let's think about those **naturalistic eyeglasses.** Some people claim that life began with a single cell and that gradually, over millions of years, sea creatures evolved, and they in turn evolved into amphibians, which later evolved into reptiles, which evolved into birds, which evolved into mammals and finally into man. Look at the picture to the right. Have you ever seen a similar picture in a book or a museum display? People with a naturalistic worldview believe that life is all part of one big tree. This view is taught in most schools, museums and publications.

14. However, those who wear **biblical glasses** believe the Word of God. When we read 'after their kind,' we don't think about a single tree. Rather, we think of an orchard of trees, each representing a different kind. For example, we have dog kinds, cat kinds, horse kinds, finch kinds and so forth. But we never have a dog kind changing into a cat kind. This is the picture we see in Genesis when God talks about creating living things 'after their kind.'

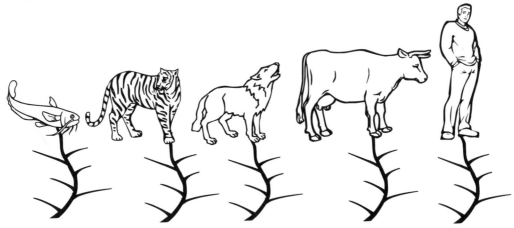

15. There is much to learn about 'created kinds.' The study of created kinds is called baraminology (another 50-cent word!). The word is taken from two Hebrew words: '*bara*,' which means 'create,' and '*min*,' the word for 'kind' that you find in the Bible.

Activity: baraminology—the creationist orchard. Your teacher will help you with an activity that will teach you about baramins and will explain created kinds more fully.

16. Draw below how you think it looked as God created **'the sea monsters, and every living creature that moves, with which the waters swarmed after their kind'** (Genesis 1:21a, NAS).

17. Draw below how you think it looked as God created

'every winged bird after its kind' (Genesis 1:21c, NAS).

Day 6 of Creation

18. On the Sixth Day, God created more living creatures. Read the verse and draw this part of His creation.

> 'Then God said, "Let the earth bring forth living creatures after their kind: cattle and creeping things and beasts of the earth after their kind"; and it was so' (Genesis 1:24, NAS).

19. God's final creation was man. Read Genesis 1:26–27 below and draw a picture of the creation of mankind. We're going to study a lot more about this part of God's creation.

> 'And God said, "Let Us make man in Our image, according to Our likeness;" … and God created man in His own image, in the image of God He created him; male and female He created them' (Genesis 1:26–27, NAS).

> 'Thus the heavens and the earth were completed, and all their hosts' (Genesis 2:1, NAS).

> 'And God saw all that He had made, and behold, it was very good' (Genesis 1:31, NAS).

7 C's Connection: _____

How old is God's world?

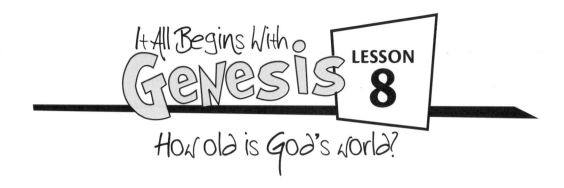

One of the biggest disagreements that people have today has to do with the age of the universe and the earth. Many people claim that the heavens and earth are millions and billions of years old. You hear this from television, from museums and from school teachers. Others claim that the Bible seems to say that the earth was created only thousands of years ago. Each person needs to study this question for himself.

Many adults have a big problem with this question. Many are Christians, and they believe the earth is very old. You won't be able to make the final decision quickly. You will have to study many things first. This week we will simply look at the word 'day' in Genesis to see what kind of 'day' it is, and we'll begin to establish a timeline from the Bible itself.

• It's time to put on those eyeglasses again. The person who has a **naturalistic** worldview *must* see the earth and entire universe as billions and millions of years old. He must have that time to make the theory of evolution in any way possible. He doesn't believe in a God who could create the universe and all kinds of life 'out of nothing,' so his only other alternative is to claim that all of life evolved over the course of billions of years. The naturalist will fight for this, and he is unable to see the world in any other way.

• The person who believes in God as Creator could believe the earth and universe are very old, or they are very young. We believe in a God who could do it any way He chooses! So, the question is ... What does the eyewitness say? Does the Bible itself say the earth is very old, or is it relatively young? Millions and billions, or thousands, of years? That's what the person with a **Biblical** worldview must ask.

Since our assignment this week is to begin to look at how old the Bible says the world and universe is, we need to start by looking at the word 'day,' a word you saw used so often in Genesis 1. Some people say that the word 'day' in Genesis 1 doesn't really mean a 24-hour day as we know it, but rather each 'day' means a very long period of time. It could mean millions and millions of years. We need to look for ourselves and try to see what Genesis 1 means when it uses the word 'day.'

1. Today we need to look at the meaning of the word 'day.' (Want to know the Hebrew? It is '*yom.*' Don't you feel smart?) Look at your observation worksheet for Genesis 1 that you have already done. Count how many times the word 'day' is used. (Did you highlight or mark them all?) What is the number?_____ 'Day' is a key word, isn't it?

2. The word 'day' could have several different meanings.

   ✓ It could mean the period of time when the sun is shining.

   'During the day I will be able to go swimming in my pool.'

OR

   ✓ It could mean the entire 24-hour period.

   'One more day and it will be Saturday.'

OR

   ✓ It could mean a general, vague point in time.

   'One day I will learn how to play the trumpet.'

3. How do you then know which meaning to give to the word?

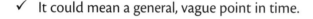

_____

_____

_____

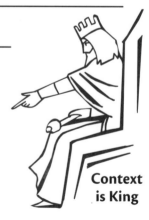

(If you answered 'context' or you wrote that you needed to see the other words surrounding the word 'day,' you are right! The word CONTEXT means 'with text.' You look for other words that surround that word and see how all those other words are put together. Context is how the Bible is woven together. Knowing the context is the only way to understand what the Bible is really saying.)

Context is King

4. Now look at **Genesis 1:4–5.** It is written out for you below. It is the first mention of the word 'day' in the whole Bible.

    'God separated the light from the darkness. And God called the light *day* and the darkness He called night' (NAS).

    As you look at the *context* of the verse, circle below what you think God means by 'day' in this verse:

    ✓   the time of day when the sun is shining—the daytime

    ✓   a regular, 24-hour day

    ✓   a general, vague point in time

5. Now look at the next time 'day' is used, in **Genesis 1:5.** It is used in still another way.

    'There was evening and there was morning—one *day*' (NAS).

    As you look at the context of the verse, circle below what you think God means by 'day' in this verse:

    ✓   the time of day when the sun is shining—the daytime

    ✓   a regular, 24-hour day

    ✓   a general, vague point in time

    This phrase is repeated over and over in Genesis 1: 'one day ... a second day ... a third day... a fourth day ... a fifth day ... the sixth day.' It must be important!

6. There is one more important way 'day' is used in Genesis. It is found in **Genesis 2:4.** It says,

   'This is the account of the heavens and the earth when they were created in the *day* that the Lord God made earth and heaven' (NAS).

   Which of the three kinds of 'day' does the *context* tell you this is?

   ✓ the time of day when the sun is shining—the daytime

   ✓ a regular, 24-hour day

   ✓ a general, vague point in time

7. In order to see the meaning of 'day' in the first chapter of Genesis, it is helpful to look at a cross-reference from the Book of Exodus. It is **Exodus 20:11.** In this passage God is giving the Ten Commandments to Moses. (We're giving you the context of this verse—the information that surrounds this verse, which helps you to understand the verse.)

   'For in six days the Lord made the heavens and the earth, the sea and all that is in them, and rested on the seventh day; therefore the Lord blessed the Sabbath day and made it holy' (NAS).

   Now, as you look at the *context* of this verse, which of the three meanings of 'day' do you think God is using? Circle the answer below.

   ✓ the time of day when the sun is shining—the daytime

   ✓ a regular, 24-hour day

   ✓ a general, vague point in time

   How can you tell? Give a reason for your answer.

   _____

   _____

8. Now that you understand about context, what would you say God means when He says He created the heavens and the earth in six days? What kind of 'day' does He seem to be indicating? Can you tell?

_____

_____

Biblical timeline of history

How long ago did God create the heavens and the earth? How many years of history does the Bible cover? Millions? Billions? Thousands? The Bible doesn't give us an exact figure. Serious students of the Bible have studied the dates given in Scripture, and they have studied the family histories and when certain people lived and died. They have also looked at history as understood by archeologists (people who have 'dug up' remains of past events).

A 'timeline' appears below. On it are dates of some of the most important happenings in the Bible. These are not exact dates, though. They have been rounded off to make them easier to remember. But they give you an idea of how long ago the events happened.

9. We have listed five important events in history below. Your assignment will be to make arrows and add these events to the timeline below. The events we want you to put on the timeline are:

   ✓ Creation—approximately 4000 years before Christ
   ✓ The Flood—approximately 2500 years before Christ
   ✓ Abraham—approximately 2000 years before Christ
   ✓ Moses and the Exodus—approximately 1500 years before Christ.
   ✓ The Present—2000 years after Christ

10. Now that you have placed the events on the timeline, add up all the numbers and write below how old the Bible seems to say the earth is.

_____

11. Do you ever wonder how Biblical scholars get these ages from the Bible? We have included parts of five passages below. Look at them briefly to see what 'clues' are given about time in each of them. You don't have to read them in detail or try to figure up the ages for yourself. You just need to see how these and many other places in Scripture are used to make timelines like the one we gave you.

   ✓ **Genesis 5:5–7** (NAS) 'So all the days that Adam lived were *nine hundred and thirty years*, and he died. And Seth lived *one hundred and five years*, and became the father of Enosh. Then Seth lived *eight hundred and seven years* after he became the father of Enosh, and he had [other] sons and daughters.'

   ✓ **Exodus 12:40–41** (NAS) 'Now the time that the sons of Israel lived in Egypt was *four hundred and thirty years*. And it came about at the end of four hundred and thirty years, to the very day, that all the hosts of the Lord went out from the land of Egypt.'

   ✓ **Matthew 1:17** (NAS) 'Therefore all the generations from Abraham to David are *fourteen generations*; and from David to the deportation to Babylon *fourteen generations*; and from the deportation to Babylon to [the time of] Christ *fourteen generations.*'

12. When you go to school or visit a museum of natural history or read the newspaper, you learn another version for how long the earth and universe have been around. Although the dates you are given vary greatly, this is what is commonly taught:

   ✓ 'big bang' origin of universe 15 billion years ago

   ✓ earth and solar system 4.5–5 billion years ago

   ✓ single-celled organisms 3–4 billion years ago

   ✓ multicelled organisms 1 billion years ago

   ✓ humans 1–3 million years ago

13. In the space below, draw a timeline or some kind of picture that shows this timeline. How does it compare with the time scale as presented in the Bible above?

14. How do you know whom to believe? Who was there when the earth began? Who was the eyewitness? (Remember the cake mystery?)

Does the rest of the Bible give us any clues?

Today we need to look at other verses in the Bible to see if they give us any clues about the amount of time that God took to create. Did He create things quickly, instantly, 'in the twinkling of an eye'?

OR

Did God create slowly, over billions of years?

15. Printed below for you is **Psalm 33:6.** Some people say this verse gives us an answer to the question.

'By the word of the Lord the heavens were made, and by the breath of His mouth all their host' (NAS).

Is there anything in this figurative language that might give you a hint?

_____

16. Now read **Psalm 148:5.** 'Let them praise the name of the Lord, for He commanded and they were created' (NAS).

    Do you think that things happened quickly or over millions of years? When a king commands, is he obeyed instantly or over a very long time?

    _____

17. Finally (to confuse things) read **2 Peter 3:8–9.** 'But do not forget this one thing, dear friends: With the Lord a day is like a thousand years, and a thousand years are like a day. The Lord is not slow in keeping his promise, as some understand slowness. He is patient with you, not wanting anyone to perish, but everyone to come to repentance' (NIV).

    Could the Scripture be referring to the length of Creation Days here?

    _____

Do you have your mind made up about the age of things yet? Probably not! There is still much to investigate from God's Word and from His world. In lessons to come we will be observing much more about the Fall, about the Flood, and about living things and rocks and fossils. Be excited about your study. It will teach you much about the wonderful God who created you and died to redeem you.

7 C's Connection: _____

It All Begins With GENESIS

LESSON 9

God's special creation: man!

Oh, how very special you are! In this week's lesson you will take a closer look at the creation of man in Genesis 2.

We will begin to look for an answer to the worldview questions 'Who am I?' and 'What is God's purpose for me?'

Is man a 'cosmic accident'?

OR

Is he a child of the King?

Ready to get started?

1. Begin your study of the creation of man by taking out your observation sheet for chapter 2, found in the back of this workbook. It's time to start hiking through chapter 2.

2. Before you read, we want you to notice something. Read **Genesis 2:1–3.**

   Can you see that these three verses are continuing the story of the Creation Week begun in chapter 1? They would probably fit better in chapter 1. (You probably know that chapters and verses weren't part of the original manuscripts of Scripture. They were added later for our convenience in studying.)

   Draw a line across the page below verse 3 so that you can see that the subject of chapter 2 doesn't really begin until after these three verses.

3. Look next at verse 4. Draw a big colored box around it. You see this statement repeated many times in the Book of Genesis. It is used to introduce the part that is coming after it. It is a KEY PHRASE.

4. Look next at your observation sheet for Genesis 5 at verse 1. Fill in the blank below.

   'These are the generations of _____.'

These words are introducing the next section of the Book of Genesis. You will see this key phrase repeated in other parts of the book as well. (Remember, when God repeats Himself, it is *important*.)

5. Now go back to chapter 2, verse 5. From there until the end of the chapter, God is telling us more about Day 6 of Creation. Day 6 is an especially important Day of Creation to God and to you, so He gives us a lot of detail about what He did and how He did it.

    Write on the line below *why* you think Day 6 of Creation is such an important day to God and to you.

    _____

6. Now it is time to go through the chapter, answering the who/what/where kinds of questions asked in the margin. This will help you understand what is in the chapter.

7. You marked some important key words on your observation sheet for chapter 2. There is a reason for doing that—it is not just a way to color and decorate the page!

    Every time you mark a key word, you can learn something about that word. It will answer one of the 'magic' who, what, where, when, why and how types of questions. You will ask the text to tell you: 'Text, what question is being answered here?' Once you learn that, you will be able to make a LIST of all the things you have learned from that word.

    So now we're going back to what you marked about God, man and woman; and you will make a list that will show you some important things about what God has done. We'll help you get started.

    God begins to talk about His creation of man in chapter 1, so you will need both observation worksheets to make this list.

Go to this verse.	**Write what you learn about God/man/woman here.**	
Genesis 1:26	God made man (how?)	
	God told man to (what?)	
Genesis 1:27	God created them (man) (what?)	

Go to this verse.   **Write what you learn about God/man/woman here.**

Genesis 1:28	God them. (Did what?)	
	God told them to (what?)	
Genesis 1:29	God told man and animals *what* to eat	
Genesis 2:7	God gives details about *how* He formed man:	
Genesis 2:15	God tells *where* He placed the man and *what* He told the man to do:	
Genesis 2:16	God gives the man an instruction and a warning (what?)	
Genesis 2:18	God says (what?)	
Genesis 2:19–20	To help the man realize that there was no suitable helper for him among the animals, God does *what*?	

Go to this verse. | **Write what you learn about God/man/woman here.**

Go to this verse.		Write what you learn about God/man/woman here.
Genesis 2:21–22	God tells *how* He formed woman:	
Genesis 2:23	Adam's reaction to seeing the woman (what?)	
Genesis 2:24–25	God introduces the institution of marriage (what?)	

8. Sum it up. Now that you have completed your chart, talk with your class about what you learned while making the list.

   What did you learn about God? Can you see any difference between the way God created the animals and the way He created man?

   _____

   _____

   Can you see why man is special? Can you see something about his purpose on earth?

   _____

   _____

7 C's Connection: _____

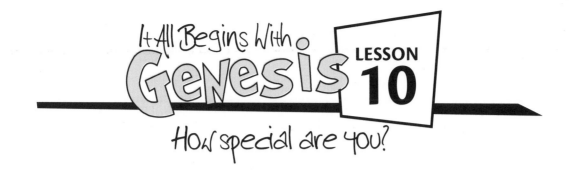

It All Begins With GENESIS

How special are you?

In the last lesson you saw how God made man—that was special! Today we are going to look at cross-references from other places in Scripture. There we will see even more about what God thinks about man. Do you remember what 'step' of inductive Bible study looks at cross-references? It is step 4—the 'satellite view.'

Remember, in inductive Bible study, we are looking at the passage and seeing what questions (who, what, where, when, why, how) are being answered.

1. **Job 33:4** (NIV) 'The Spirit of God has made me; the breath of the Almighty gives me life.'

    Write below *who* gave you life.

    _____

2. **Psalm 100:3** (NIV) 'Know that the LORD is God. It is he who made us, and not we ourselves; we are his people, the sheep of his pasture.'

    Write below *who* made us. *What* does that make us?

    _____

    _____

3. **Psalm 119:73** (NIV) 'Your hands made me and formed me; give me understanding to learn your commands.'

    Write below *what* God did to you. *What* should you do because of what God did?

    _____

    _____

    _____

4. **Isaiah 43:6b–7** (NIV) 'Bring my sons from afar and my daughters from the ends of the earth—everyone who is called by my name, whom I created for my glory, whom I formed and made.'

Write below *what* God did for you. *Why* did He do it?

_____

_____

_____

5. **Isaiah 64:8** (NIV) 'Yet, O LORD, you are our Father. We are the clay, you are the potter; we are all the work of your hand.'

Write below *who* God is and *who* we are.

_____

_____

_____

6. Read the passage below. As you read, draw a stick figure for every mention of man.

Psalm 8:3–9 (NIV) 'When I consider your heavens, the work of your fingers, the moon and the stars, which you have set in place, what is man that you are mindful of him, the son of man that you care for him? You made him a little lower than the heavenly beings and crowned him with glory and honor. You made him ruler over the works of your hands; you put everything under his feet: all flocks and herds, and the beasts of the field, the birds of the air, and the fish3 of the sea, all that swim the paths of the seas. O LORD, our Lord, how majestic is your name in all the earth.'

Write below *what* God thinks of man and *what* God has given man to do.

_____

_____

_____

_____

_____

_____

7. **John 3:16** (NIV) 'For God so loved the world that he gave his one and only Son, that whoever believes in him shall not perish but have eternal life.'

   Write below *what* God did. *Why* did He do what He did? *What* was the result of that action?

   _____

   _____

   _____

8. According to God's Word, *why* were you created? (Hint: Look at Isaiah 43:6-7 again.)

   _____

   _____

We are told to live for the glory of God. Do you know what that means? It means you should do the things that God wants you to do, the things that honor Him. You are to do the things that please God. Also, you do those things the way God wants you to do them, the way He tells you in His Word.

9. What are you doing now for the glory of God? (Is He pleased?)

_____

_____

10. What do you see in your life that you need to change in order to live for the glory of God?

_____

_____

Before we stop for today, let's consider again the two different worldviews people have when they look at man.

11. The person who wears naturalistic eyeglasses (the naturalistic worldview) believes that man is an accident. Man is just another animal who happened to evolve from other animals that also happened by accident. Pretend for a moment that you are that person. How would you answer the following?

✓ What is the purpose of my life?

_____

_____

_____

✓ How do I decide what to do and what is right or wrong?

_____

_____

12. The person who wears Biblical eyeglasses (the biblical worldview) knows that God has created him in His own image. Answer the questions below from that worldview perspective.

✓ What is the purpose of my life?

_____

_____

_____

✓ How do I decide what to do and what is right or wrong?

_____

_____

_____

_____

7 C's Connection: _____

Life before sin came into the world

When God created the world, it was an ideal world—God's ideal. In this lesson we are going to look at the world God created, a world without sin. None of us has ever experienced this kind of world, and Genesis 1 and 2 tell us what it was like.

We need to understand these things in order to have a Biblical worldview about the pain, suffering and other problems of the world we live in.

You will need to refer to your observation worksheets for chapters 1 and 2 to answer these questions.

1. What did God say about the world He had created? Read Genesis 1:31.

    _____

2. Go to your observation worksheet for Genesis 2. Mark every mention of the key word 'garden.' (You may wish to color it green or draw a green 'bush' around the word.) Then in the space below, make a list of what you learn about this Garden.

    _____

    _____

    _____

    _____

    _____

    _____

    _____

You have been given a page at the back of this lesson on which to draw how you visualize the world before sin. Take a moment now to go to the page and draw what you have learned so far from marking 'garden.'

3. Imagine what life was like for Adam and Eve before they sinned. What was the relationship between Adam and Eve? Did they talk to each other? Did they fight? What does **Genesis 2:23–25** tell us about their relationship?

    _____

    _____

    _____

4. Now, let's look at their relationship to God. Did they talk to Him and did He talk to them? Did they spend time with Him often? You'll have to go to your observation sheet and find **Genesis 3:8** to answer. Write your answer below. (Note: Genesis 3 was written after the Fall. However, the first part of the verse tells you something that obviously had been going on before the sin happened.)

    _____

    _____

    _____

5. Did God give Adam and Eve any work to do, or did they just sit around watching TV all day? Check it out in **Genesis 1:26–28** and write below what you learn.

    _____

    _____

    _____

6. What did Adam and Eve and all the animals eat while in the Garden? Check out **Genesis 1:29–30.**

    _____

    _____

7. Does that mean that big cats, velociraptors, eagles, and other carnivores (meat-eaters) didn't eat each other before the Fall? (Hmmm … a tough question but interesting to consider!)

_____

8. What do you think the weather was like in this world before the Fall? Can you tell if there were bad storms, snow and earthquakes? (You can get some ideas about this from **Genesis 2:5–6, 9–15, 25.**) Write your ideas below.

_____

_____

_____

_____

_____

9. Do you think Adam and Eve would have lived forever if they had not sinned? Look at **Genesis 2:9, 17** and **3:22** to find out.

_____

_____

_____

_____

10. Do you think there was pain, sorrow or suffering before the Fall? Look again at **Genesis 1:31** and answer below.

_____

_____

Now that you have looked at some more aspects of their life before the Fall, go again to your drawing and add anything new you have seen.

A good way to understand God's perfect creation before the Fall is to see what He says about the future state of the earth after Christ returns. God's Word talks about this future state in lots of places. We are going to look at two Bible references. Even though they don't describe the pre-Fall world exactly, they do give us an idea about what God thinks is very good.

11. Read **Isaiah 11:6–9** (NIV). 'The wolf will live with the lamb, the leopard will lie down with the goat, the calf and the lion and the yearling [will feed] together; and a little child will lead them. The cow will feed with the bear, their young will lie down together, and the lion will eat straw like the ox. The infant will play near the hole of the cobra, and the young child put his hand into the viper's nest. They will neither harm nor destroy on all my holy mountain, for the earth will be full of the knowledge of the LORD as the waters cover the sea.'

    (Use words from the text, not merely 'yes' or 'no' answers.)

    ✓ Will animals eat each other? _____

    ✓ Will man and animals be afraid of each other? _____

    ✓ What will the lion and ox eat?_____

    ✓ Will there be hurting or destroying? _____

    ✓ Will everyone know God? _____

12. **Revelation 21:1 to 22:5** is a long but wonderful passage that speaks of God's new creation. If you can, it would be helpful for you to read the whole passage. But if not, we include a few of the verses below to show you some parallels. When we find parallels, we see things that are similar in more than one place. The Bible has lots of parallels. The following parallels show you what God considers good in the things He creates.

    ✓ Look at **Revelation 21:3** (NIV). 'And I heard a loud voice from the throne saying, "Now the dwelling of God is with men, and he will live with them. They will be his people, and God himself will be with them and be their God." '

Write below how Revelation 21:3 reminds you of the time in the Garden of Eden before the Fall.

_____

_____

✓ Now read **Revelation 21:4** (NIV). 'He will wipe every tear from their eyes. There will be no more death or mourning or crying or pain, for the old order of things has passed away.'

What is God's ideal concerning death and suffering? If God created a 'very good' world, what would it have been like in the Garden?

_____

_____

✓ What do you see in the following passage that was also present in the pre-Fall world? Circle it below.

Revelation 22:1–2 (NIV). 'Then the angel showed me the river of the water of life, as clear as crystal, flowing from the throne of God and of the Lamb down the middle of the great street of the city. On each side of the river stood the tree of life, bearing twelve crops of fruit, yielding its fruit every month. And the leaves of the tree are for the healing of the nations.'

✓ What else do you see that was also true in the pre-Fall world? Read this passage and highlight your answer.

Revelation 22:3–4 (NIV) 'No longer will there be any curse. The throne of God and of the Lamb will be in the city, and his servants will serve him. They will see his face, and his name will be on their foreheads.'

✓ Check out **Revelation 21:23** (NIV). 'The city does not need the sun or the moon to shine on it, for the glory of God gives it light, and the Lamb is its lamp.'

Was it necessary when God originally created the world to have the sun or moon to give light to the world?

_____

✓ Finally, read this passage and answer the question below.

Revelation 22:5 (NIV) 'There will be no more night. They will not need the light of a lamp or the light of the sun, for the Lord God will give them light. And they will reign forever and ever.'

What are God's people going to do in Revelation 22:5 that they would have done if sin hadn't come into the world?

_____

Now that you have observed from Scripture what life was like in the Garden of Eden and have looked at the future new heavens and earth to see what God's ideal world will be, add anything you wish to your picture of life before sin came into the world. (Remember, these Scriptures have been talking about the future. Include only things that repeat something also talked about in the Garden of Eden.)

7 C's Connection: _____

Life before sin came into the world

It All Begins With Genesis — LESSON 12

Recognizing different worldviews in Scripture (part 1)

As we've studied the beginning of all things in Genesis, we've been addressing the different views people have about the world—their worldviews. You have already learned about the different 'eyeglasses' people wear—naturalistic or biblical.

In today's lesson, we will study more about how different worldviews are shown in the Bible. In other lessons to come, we will see them in the science classroom and in life all around us today.

It is extremely important to be able to recognize these views in action: it shows us 'where people are coming from,' and it helps to keep us from being deceived.

1. Before we continue, you need to be sure you understand what a particular word means. The word is

PRESUPPOSITION

Do you know what that means?

'Pre-' means 'before' or 'ahead of.' When you watch a 'preview' of a movie, you are seeing some of the movie before you view the whole thing.

'Supposition' is from the word 'suppose.' When you suppose something, you believe it is true. You take it for granted.

A *presupposition* is something you learned some time ago, and you carry that idea with you wherever you go. It is something you believe, or take for granted. You might not even know you have that idea. It may be buried so deep in you that you don't know it's there. Then, when you observe something new in the world, you understand your new observation in the light of that previous idea you had.

2. This is an example of a presupposition:

You see a dog—we'll call him 'Mop.' Now, let's pretend you have a *presupposition*. You have always thought dogs were very mean and would attack you whenever they saw you. So, how would you act then when you saw Mop? You would probably run away from him and hide. Even though he is a nice dog, the idea you *pre*-supposed made you see him in a different way.

Pretend now that your friend Bob has a *different* presupposition about dogs. He thinks dogs are loving and always good. So, how would he act when he saw Mop? He would go up to him and pet him.

You can see that the ideas you have deep within you are very important in how you act and what you think about the things around you.

3. Let's think some more about other presuppositions you might have. Write your answers on the lines below.

    ✓ When you think about your mother, what do you already believe about her? (I hope you already have a presupposition that she loves you very much.)

    _____

    ✓ So, because of what you already believe about her, what would you do if she asked you to do something for her?

    _____

    _____

4. Let's try another one.

    ✓ When Christmas is coming, what presuppositions do you have? (Perhaps you think it will be a fun time, and that you will put up decorations.)

    _____

    _____

    ✓ So then, how do you act when you realize it is almost Christmas again?

    _____

    _____

    _____

5. Let's try one more example of a presupposition.

   ✓ When you realize that a new school year is about to begin, what are your presuppositions? (Maybe you are thinking it will be lots of fun learning new things; or maybe you are afraid because you have had problems doing your schoolwork.)

   _____

   ✓ Because of what you already believe about school, how does that make you feel and act the night before school starts?

   _____

It is just as if everybody in the world had a special set of tinted eyeglasses they wear. Each set of eyeglasses is a little different, because each person has different *presuppositions.* Those previously held ideas cause them to look at their world in a certain way. That is called their *worldview.*

6. You have already been hearing about worldviews. Do you remember the definition? Just for review, here it is again.

A WORLDVIEW IS …

   A total way of looking at the world.

A WORLDVIEW IS …

   What you believe, the way you understand what the world is all about.

A WORLDVIEW IS …

   The 'big picture' of life. It helps you to understand all the individual pieces.

Some questions that your worldview answers include: (fill in the blanks)

How did the world _____?

Is there a _____?

If there is a _____, what is He _____?

How did I _____?

Who am I?

What is my _____ in life?

Where did evil _____?

How then should _____?

7. There are many different worldviews. So far in this course, we have been talking about two important worldviews, or two different pairs of eyeglasses through which people look at the world.

    Just for review, write below the two different worldviews we have been studying:

    _____. Everything came about through *time*, *chance* and *natural processes* now operating in the world. No God is necessary.

    _____. God created all things. Everywhere we see *plan*, *purpose* and *intelligent design*.

8. Now, please put on your *naturalistic* eyeglasses. Pretend you don't know anything about Jesus and you certainly don't believe in miracles.

We're going to 'role play' something that the Apostle John wrote in his Gospel. It is recorded in **John 2:1–10.** If you have enough people in your class, choose people to play the following parts: the narrator, Jesus, Mary, the master (he is like the caterer in charge) of the feast, the bridegroom and the servants. You will need to find some prop stone pots and a cup for 'tasting' the 'wine.' Act out the event together, and then answer the questions that follow. We have written out the script of the play for you to follow.

Narrator: On the third day a wedding took place at Cana in Galilee. Jesus' mother was there, and Jesus and his disciples had also been invited to the wedding. When the wine was gone, Jesus' mother said to him ... (verses 2–3)

Mary: 'They have no more wine.' (verse 3)

Jesus: 'Dear woman, why do you involve me? My time has not yet come.' (verse 4)

Mary: (said to the servants) 'Do whatever He tells you.' (verse 5)

Narrator: Nearby stood six stone water jars, the kind used by the Jews for ceremonial washing, each holding from twenty to thirty gallons. (verse 6)

Jesus: (said to the servants) 'Fill the jars with water.' (verse 7)

Servants: (Fill six stone jars to the brim.)

Jesus: (to the servants after they fill the pots) 'Now draw some out and take it to the master of the banquet.' (verse 8)

Servants: (Take some water out and put it in a goblet and take it to the master of the banquet.)

Master of banquet: (Taste the water that has been turned into wine. React when you taste such a wonderful flavor.) (verse 9)

Narrator: The master of the banquet did not know where the new wine had come from, although the servants who had drawn the water knew. (verse 9)

Master of banquet: (Motion for the bridegroom to come to your side.) 'Everyone brings out the choice wine first and then the cheaper wine after the guests have had too much to drink; but you have saved the best till now.' (verse 10)

Narrator: This is the first of the miraculous signs that Jesus performed at Cana in Galilee. He thus revealed His glory, and His disciples put their faith in Him. (verse 11)

9. See if you can answer the following questions about the master of the banquet.

   ✓ Did the master of the banquet like the 'wine' when he tasted it? (See verse 10.)

   _____

   ✓ How old was the wine that Jesus made? (seconds? minutes? days? months?) (See verses 7–9.)

   _____

   ✓ How old did the master of the banquet think the wine was?

   _____

   ✓ Was his reasoning reasonable? _____

   ✓ Was his reasoning correct? _____

   ✓ What kind of 'eyeglasses' was he wearing? What worldview directed his thinking?

   _____

   ✓ Can you think of any 'hints' that the master of the banquet might have noted that indicated something different or unusual was going on here?

   _____

   _____

   ✓ Is there any way the master of the banquet might have learned the true story of the wine? Who were the eyewitnesses? Could he have avoided his mistake? (Hint: verses 6, 9)

   _____

   _____

   _____

If you were the master of the banquet at that wedding, would you have thought the same thing? Sure! His reasoning was 'reasonable.' He was wearing naturalistic eyeglasses. He never even considered questioning this strange happening. He didn't talk to the eyewitnesses. (The servants who filled the pots knew all about it!) He didn't know or think that God could do something miraculous. His *presupposition* was that wine always comes by slow, natural processes.

10. Think for a moment about the following statement:

When God creates something, it may look like it took a long time.

Hmmm ... could that be true? And if it is true, what difference does it make? The next few questions should show you what we mean.

   ✓ How long did the master of the banquet think it took for the wine to be made?

   Circle: weeks   hours   minutes   seconds

   ✓ How long did it *actually* take for Jesus to make the wine?

   Circle: weeks   hours   minutes   seconds

   ✓ Here is another example: When God created Adam, he was a grown man. If you didn't *know* that God created him, you would have thought Adam began in his mother's womb and was then a baby and then a child and then a teenager and finally a grown-up. When you wear naturalistic eyeglasses, that is what you would see. But God created him as a grown-up, in an instant!

   ✓ One more example: When God created the trees, they didn't begin as little seeds. They already had fruit on them! But if you had not been there to see God creating them, how old would you think the trees might be?

   _____

Try to remember this when we look at things in God's world that seem to have come about by natural processes. God works through natural processes, but He also works miraculously, as we see often in Scripture.

When we hear 'reasonable' explanations, we need to evaluate them in the light of Scripture (the eyewitness). We need to examine the evidence carefully.

Where did the master of the banquet go wrong?

- ✓ His presupposition was that everything happens naturalistically. He didn't even consider there could be another way.

- ✓ He did not consult the eyewitnesses.

- ✓ He wouldn't consider any evidence that could show his thinking was wrong.

11. Write below at least one important thing you learned from this lesson.

_____

_____

_____

_____

_____

7 C's Connection: _____

Recognizing different worldviews in Scripture (Part 2)

In this lesson, we will look at a very important passage of Scripture. It will teach you something about Creation as well as something about those who view the world with naturalistic eyeglasses.

1. **Romans 1:18–32** is printed out for you below. This is a difficult passage, but one of the most important in Scripture. We're going to study this passage inductively this week. It teaches more about the naturalistic worldview. It also tells us something about what God's creation shows us. Please read it carefully, and mark the words as instructed:

   Mark 'God' and all references to Him with a *purple crown*.

   Mark 'men' and all references to men by drawing a *blue box* or *stick figure*.

(NIV) 18 'The wrath of God is being revealed from heaven against all the godlessness and wickedness of men who suppress the truth by their wickedness, 19 since what may be known about God is plain to them, because God has made it plain to them. 20 For since the creation of the world God's invisible qualities—his eternal power and divine nature—have been clearly seen, being understood from what has been made, so that men are without excuse. 21 For although they knew God, they neither glorified him as God nor gave thanks to him, but their thinking became futile and their foolish hearts were darkened. 22 Although they claimed to be wise, they became fools 23 and exchanged the glory of the immortal God for images made to look like mortal man and birds and animals and reptiles. 24 Therefore God gave them over in the sinful desires of their hearts to sexual impurity for the degrading of their bodies with one another. 25 They exchanged the truth of God for a lie, and worshiped and served created things rather than the Creator—who is forever praised. Amen. 26 Because of this, God gave them over to shameful lusts. Even their women exchanged natural relations for unnatural ones. 27 In the same way the men also abandoned natural relations with women and were inflamed with lust for one another. Men committed indecent acts with other men, and received in themselves the due penalty for their perversion. 28 Furthermore, since they did not think it worthwhile to retain the knowledge of God, he gave them over to a depraved mind, to do what ought not to be done. 29 They have become filled with every kind of wickedness, evil, greed and depravity. They are full of envy, murder, strife, deceit and malice.

30 They are gossips, slanderers, God-haters, insolent, arrogant and boastful; they invent ways of doing evil; they disobey their parents; 31 they are senseless, faithless, heartless, ruthless. 32 Although they know God's righteous decree that those who do such things deserve death, they not only continue to do these very things but also approve of those who practice them.'

2. *What* three things do we learn about God from studying His creation? (Look at verse 20.)

    1. _____

    2. _____

    3. _____

3. *How* does Paul describe the men in verse 18, and *what* does he say they are doing?

    _____

    _____

    _____

4. Is God angry about it? *How* do you know from verse 18?

    _____

    _____

5. Do they have any excuse for what they have done (verse 20)?

    _____

6. *What* did they do that made God so angry (verses 21–21)?

    _____

    _____

    _____

7. In verses 24, 26 and 28, we see a key repeated phrase. Mark it in a distinctive way. What is the phrase?

    _____

8. *What* is it that God gave them over to? Write some of the results below.

_____

_____

_____

9. Do we still see people doing the same things today? (It's an obvious question, of course.)

_____

10. *What* kind of worldview do those people have, naturalistic or Biblical?

_____

11. Does a worldview matter? Does it really matter what someone thinks, what presuppositions they hold? Does it matter whether your worldview includes the God of the Bible in day-to-day life around us? Your teacher really wants to hear what you think and why. Please write below whether a worldview matters and why.

_____

_____

_____

_____

_____

_____

_____

7 C's Connection: _____

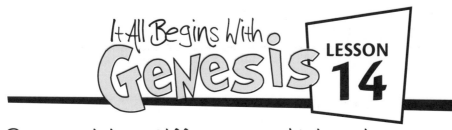

Recognizing different worldviews in our culture

Today we're going to visit three very interesting people. They represent three major worldviews we see around us today. So far in our study, we have looked at two major worldviews, naturalistic and Biblical. In the lesson today we are going to add one other worldview to our discussion. This is a view that is very prominent today—it is called the 'transcendental' or 'pantheistic' view. We'll explain it for you when we get there.

We would like to introduce you to our three guests today:

PROFESSOR GREEN is a *naturalist*. Another name he is called is a *modernist*. Below are the presuppositions he holds. (Do you remember the definition of 'presupposition'? A presupposition is something someone already believes to be true.)

- He believes there is no God. He claims that man invented God.

- He believes that matter (what we can touch, feel, prove or study) is all that exists.

- He believes that man is only matter and has no soul or spirit.

- He believes that there is no such thing as the supernatural.

- He believes that everything came into existence through time, chance and natural processes.

- He believes that truth is limited to what can be verified by experience or independent thought.

BARRY BIBLE is a *theist*. He has a Biblical worldview. These are the presuppositions he holds:

- He believes in the existence of an intelligent, powerful, loving, just and awesome God who exists in the Trinity of Father, Son and Holy Spirit.

- He believes that God created all things.

- He believes that God so loved the world that He sent His only begotten Son to die on the Cross, so that all who believe in Him can have everlasting life.

- He believes that God is the ultimate Judge.

- He believes that God reveals Himself in the Scriptures. The Scriptures are true and give people absolute truth to live by.

- He believes that we see plan, purpose and intelligent design in the cosmos.

POST-MODERN MADGE is a *pantheist*, or *transcendentalist*. That's probably a new word to you, but she represents a significant and increasing portion of today's society. What she believes is often called postmodernism. Postmodernists can believe all sorts of things, but here are a few of Madge's presuppositions:

- She doesn't believe there is any real truth. Each person has his own truth, and it changes constantly. All is relative.

- Everything is possible, but nothing is necessary. There aren't any absolutes. She tunes in to her 'inner self' to follow what seems best to her at the moment. She is free!

- She is very spiritual. She believes all things are divine. There is a part of god in people, rocks, trees, stars, etc.

- She believes there is no one way to god. All paths ultimately lead to god.

- God is impersonal, above good and evil.

- All is one and all is god. We must get in touch with the 'god within' in order to achieve true cosmic unity.

- History is cyclical. Madge believes in reincarnation.

Now that you have met our three guests, we are going to interview them. In the spaces below you will find a question followed by three different answers. See if you can tell who might have given that particular answer. Write B (Biblical), N (naturalist), or T (transcendentalist) under the words that are spoken.

How does one find his way to God?	Jesus is the way. No man comes to the Father but by Him.	There are many ways to god. All is god.	There is no God. Man invented Him.
When you go outside on a beautiful fall day, what do you see?	I see Mother Nature! Look at all the wonders of evolution. It is amazing what has developed over all these billions of years.	I see the awesome creation of an awesome God. The whole creation shouts out His glory! I also see a fallen world. There are sad things here because man fell into sin.	I see the Force! God everywhere! He is in the rocks, the trees and the birds. We are all divine, and we are one with nature.
How did life happen?	In the beginning God created the heavens and the earth.	It just happened! It came from primordial ooze and evolved upward over billions of years.	We call it cosmic evolution. There is this mysterious force that has been around from eternity, recycling its power, going from disharmony to harmony.
How can you know something is true?	We know from human reason, experience, modern science and rational thought.	There is no truth. What is true for you might not be true for me. As long as it is meaningful to *you*, that is what really matters.	Jesus is the Truth. God has revealed truth to us in the Scriptures and through His Holy Spirit.
Just who is man?	He is a highly evolved animal.	He is a spiritual being who is a god. He is fundamentally perfect.	He is a creature made in the image of God and precious to God. He is also a sinner in need of God's salvation.

What do you believe is responsible for all the crime we see today?	Poor choices. You decide the value of life based on your culture. Our society stifles our knowledge of the god within. Our culture ignores human potential.	Crime is the result of sinners in rebellion against a holy God.	It is the fault of society. There is so much ignorance and superstition. More education and more money should solve the problems.
How do you understand the problem of racism?	We are all descended from Noah and his sons—we are one family. There is no basis for racial discrimination. All Christians are one in Christ Jesus.	The group identity is all that is important. It is how we identify with our culture. It is important to connect with your group.	It is an evolutionary thing. Some groups have climbed higher in the evolutionary scale than others, while others are basically inferior. We need education and a stronger government to stop the problems that arise.

What is your view of the Bible?	It is not true. Primitive men wrote it. It is full of myths and stories. The only things that we can accept are what man discovers by reason today. Science, not an ancient book, must show us the way.	It is the revealed, true Word of God.	It is basically irrational. Religion is a choice. There are many ways to god. If the Bible is good for some, that is fine.
How can humans solve their problems today?	By scientific technology and advancement. By spending more money.	By a transformation of consciousness. Simply by love.	By salvation—by faith in the finished work of Christ.

How did you do? Can you see how people's presuppositions affect what they do in life?

Who has the most convincing answers?

As we continue to study Genesis, we'll see that the biblical approach is the only one that makes sense out of all we see around us.

7 C's Connection: _____

Recognizing different worldviews in science (part 1)

Origin of the universe

In the next five lessons, we are going to look at science.

'Hmmm,' you ask. 'Why are we looking at science when we are studying the Bible? Aren't the two separate realms that must never be considered together? Don't we read and hear that science and religion should be kept apart?'

So glad you asked. Science involves acquiring knowledge about the world, doesn't it?

And isn't it all God's world?

And isn't all truth God's truth?

1. The National Science Teachers Association gives this definition of 'science'. Read it and see if you can tell what presuppositions the writers of this definition hold.

    'Science is a method of explaining the natural world … . Because science is limited to explaining the natural world by means of natural processes, it cannot use supernatural causation in its explanations. Similarly, science is precluded from making statements about supernatural forces, because these are outside its provenance … .' (Hey, whose world *is* this, anyway?)

    What worldview is behind this definition? _____

2. Read the definition of science below, given by the PCA Origins Study commission in their report to the General Assembly in 2000.

    'The sciences are disciplines that study features of the world around us, looking for regularities as well as attempting to account for causal relations. In the causal chains we allow all relevant factors (including supernatural ones) to be considered.'

What presuppositions (naturalistic or biblical) do you see behind this definition?

_____

3. Think for a moment about the person who doesn't believe in God, who looks at the universe through naturalistic eyeglasses.

    How might he explain the origin of the planets, stars and galaxies? How long would it take? In the space below, take a crack at writing an explanation that doesn't include God.

    _____

    _____

    _____

    _____

4. The following is the currently popular naturalistic expression of the origin of the universe:

    'The "Big Bang" model of the history of the universe suggests that the universe expanded outward from a very small, hot ball of energy. At the present rate of expansion, the Big Bang would have occurred between 10–20 billion years ago.

    'The universe is self-contained and determined completely by the laws of science. The universe evolves according to well defined laws.' (Stephen Hawking)

5. Okay, does that sound reasonable? Maybe. But let's see if there is any other way to look at the universe. Let's ask some hard questions, such as 'How does an explosion produce an orderly universe?' 'Could time and chance and natural laws do the job?' 'Is there anything about the universe that looks like it was designed?'

6. In your class this week, we will talk about something called the anthropic principle. Put on your Biblical eyeglasses.

    The *anthropic principle* says that the universe appears

    _____

    _____

7. **Matching scramble game.** After you have listened to all the facts about the universe given in the game, see if you can write down the answer to the three statements that follow:

a. IF the moon was much nearer to the earth . . . THEN

_____

_____

_____

b. IF the earth was not tilted 23 degrees on its axis, but was 90 degrees in reference to the sun . . . THEN

_____

_____

c. IF we couldn't count on the constant laws of the universe, such as the law of gravity being here tomorrow . . . THEN

_____

_____

8. Biblical eyeglasses, or naturalistic? Is there any difference in the two ways of looking at the origin of the universe? They both may appear reasonable, but they both can't be right. Which explanation is more convincing to you? Why?

_____

_____

_____

9. Now let's consult the eyewitness report and see what we learn. Read the Scriptures below and answer the Five W's and H questions for each:

✓ **Genesis 1:16** (NIV) 'God made two great lights—the greater light to govern the day and the lesser light to govern the night. He also made the stars.'

What part of the universe did God make? Underline or highlight it in the text.

✓ **Nehemiah 9:6** (NIV) 'You alone are the LORD. You made the heavens, even the highest heavens, and all their starry host, the earth and all that is on it, the seas and all that is in them. You give life to everything, and the multitudes of heaven worship you.'

What did God make? Underline it above. *What* then should we do in response when we see what a great God we have? Write it below:

_____

✓ **Isaiah 40:22** (NIV) 'He sits enthroned above the circle of the earth, and its people are like grasshoppers. He stretches out the heavens like a canopy, and spreads them out like a tent to live in.'

How is the earth described in this verse? _____

Does the Bible teach a 'flat earth'? _____

What does God do to the heavens? _____

Does that statement agree or disagree with the observation by astronomers of an expanding universe? (circle agree or disagree)

✓ **Job 9:9** (NIV) 'He is the Maker of the Bear and Orion, the Pleiades and the constellations of the south.'

How did the stars form into constellations?

_____

✓ **Isaiah 40:26** (NIV) 'Lift your eyes and look to the heavens: who created all these? He who brings out the starry host one by one, and calls them each by name.'

What extraordinary thing does God do to the stars? *Why* is that so amazing? *What* does this tell us about our Creator?

_____

_____

_____

✓ **Jeremiah 32:17** (NIV) 'Ah, Sovereign LORD, you have made the heavens and the earth by your great power and outstretched arm. Nothing is too hard for you.'

What do we know about our LORD from observing His creation of the heavens and the earth? Underline or highlight the answer and then think about what that means for your life.

✓ **Hebrews 11:3** (NIV) 'By faith we understand that the universe was formed at God's command, so that what is seen was not made out of what was visible.'

How was the universe formed? _____

_____

From *what* did God make the things we see? _____

_____

How can we understand these things? _____

10. What will you believe?

7 C's Connection: _____

Recognizing different worldviews in science (part 2)

Origin of the rock layers and fossils of the earth

Rocks and fossils—fascinating studies! Have you ever been to Grand Canyon to see the layer-cake rock formations? Have you heard the story given by the rangers about how they formed? Even on vacation you need to be ready to discern naturalistic presuppositions.

1. Consider once more the person who does not believe in God or in Scripture. How would this person describe how the earth's geology came to be—the rock layers, the fossils, the mountains and valleys? Try to come up with a reasonable explanation from that point of view.

    _____

    _____

    _____

2. The following words are some you would probably hear from the park ranger at Grand Canyon. Do they sound reasonable? What kind of eyeglasses is he wearing?

    The principle of uniformity states that processes that occurred in past times produced the same results as similar processes do today (sedimentation, erosion, etc.). Therefore, the sediments that formed the rock layers were deposited in the past as they are today. (For example: 1 ft of sediment = approximately 5,000–10,000 years per ft)

    The deeper you go, the older the rock layers are.

    Fossils are the remains or traces of plants and animals that lived in the past.

    The rock record reveals the evolution of life throughout millions of years as the index fossils of each layer are identified.

3. The naturalistic explanation of the rocks and fossils you have just read is called 'uniformitarianism.' (Another 50-cent word for you to learn!) You will see this explanation in all your school textbooks, in museums, on TV documentaries and when you visit national parks. But is there another way of looking at it, a way that agrees with the Bible's teaching about the world?

Glad you asked! This biblical way of looking at the rocks and fossils is called 'catastrophism' (another 50-cent word). Catastrophism is the theory that a major portion of the rocks and fossils of the earth was formed as a result of a watery global catastrophe that lasted years instead of millions of years.

Just so you'll remember, write below the definitions of uniformitarianism and catastrophism.

Definition of uniformitarianism (naturalistic)

_____

_____

_____

_____

Definition of catastrophism (biblical)

_____

_____

_____

_____

4. **Column 'sand or rice' activity.** Your teacher will demonstrate with this activity two ways that the layers of rock we see around us today could have been formed. The chart on the next page will help you follow the demonstration, and you can write some notes on the chart to help you remember what is said.

Sedimentary rocks and fossils—two ways to explain them

Naturalistic uniformitarianism		Biblical catastrophism
	9. Cretaceous. *Large dinosaurs; flowering plants and trees; dinosaurs disappear later*	
	8. Jurassic. *Reptiles dominant, many huge; rodent-like mammals*	
	7. Triassic. *Dinosaurs; lush forests of cone-bearing trees and palm-like trees; ichthyosaurs and plesiosaurs*	
	6. Permian. *Many reptiles and amphibians*	
	5. Carboniferous. *Coal and oil; amphibians; fish; insects, such as cockroaches and dragonflies; lizards*	
	4. Devonian. *Vertebrate fishes; amphibians; large land plants, such as ferns*	
	3. Silurian. *Invertebrate and vertebrate marine animals; starfish; spiders on land; land plants*	
	2. Ordovician. *Brachiopods; snails; mollusks; coral; early vertebrate fish*	
	1. Cambrian. *Explosion of a variety of marine life, invertebrates, trilobites and brachiopods*	

5. **Fossil activity.** Those sedimentary rock layers are full of fossils. Have you ever thought about what is needed to make a fossil? Your teacher will take you through this fun activity.

   When you look at this fossil of a fish swallowing a fish, what does that tell you about how fossils are usually formed?

6. Have things always continued the same throughout the history of the world? Is there anything that has happened in history that was vastly different from what we experience today—something that would cause great geologic upheavals and cause the formation of fossils? Read the following Scriptures that give the eyewitness report; and answer the who, what, where, when, why and how questions given.

   ✓ **Genesis 7:11** (NIV) 'In the six hundredth year of Noah's life, on the seventeenth day of the second month—on that day all the springs of the great deep burst forth, and the floodgates of the heavens were opened.'

   Genesis 7:17–24 (NIV) 'For forty days the flood kept coming on the earth, and as the waters increased they lifted the ark high above the earth. The waters rose and increased greatly on the earth, and the ark floated on the surface of the water. They rose greatly on the earth, and all the high mountains under the entire heavens were covered. The waters rose and covered the mountains to a depth of more than twenty feet. Every living thing that moved on the earth perished—birds, livestock, wild animals, all the creatures that swarm over the earth, and all mankind. Everything on dry land that had the breath of life in its nostrils died. Every living thing on the face of the earth was wiped out; men and animals and the creatures that move along the ground and the birds of the air were wiped from the earth. Only Noah was left, and those with him in the ark. The waters flooded the earth for a hundred and fifty days.'

   How deep was the water of the Flood? _____

   _____

   _____

   What happened to the living things on the earth? _____

   _____

   _____

✓ **2 Peter 3:3–6** (NIV) 'First of all, you must understand that in the last days scoffers will come, scoffing and following their own evil desires. They will say, "Where is this 'coming' he promised? Ever since our fathers died, everything goes on as it has since the beginning of creation." But they deliberately forget that long ago by God's word the heavens existed and the earth was formed out of water and by water. By these waters also the world of that time was deluged and destroyed.'

In 2 Peter 3:3, the Apostle Peter points out that there will be people who will make fun of the idea that Christ is going to return, and they will say that all things continue the same from Creation until the present. Peter points out that they are deliberately ignoring an event that changed everything.

What are the 'scoffers' forgetting, which happened according to God's Word?

_____

_____

_____

7. Is there a difference between these two ways of looking at the earth's geology and fossils? Which will you believe?

7 C's Connection: _____

Recognizing different worldviews in science (part 3)

Life—how did it begin?

After the universe came into being, there had to be a time when that first living cell appeared. How did that happen? How did life come to be?

1. Once again, try to think like a person who does not believe in God. All you have is human reasoning to understand something that happened through naturalistic laws and processes. Try to come up with a reasonable explanation about the origin of the first living things and write it below. Be creative!

    _____

    _____

    _____

2. Following is a quotation from a popular high-school biology textbook. (*Biology Principles*, Holt, p. 227)

    > 'Most scientists think that life on earth had a spontaneous origin, developing by itself through natural chemical and physical processes. They hypothesize that molecules of nonliving matter reacted chemically during the first one billion years of earth's history, forming a variety of simple organic molecules, some of which were capable of replicating themselves [and they] formed associations that became increasingly complex. In laboratory experiments, many of the organic building blocks of life have been made from molecules of nonliving matter.'

    Is this paragraph anything like what you came up with? _____

    Does it sound reasonable? _____

    What kind of eyeglasses are the writers of this textbook wearing?

    _____

3. Is there another way of looking at the origin of life?

    Is there any way to see whether something is formed by natural laws and chance *or* by an intelligent designer?

    Consider the following:

    *   Which one of the items pictured below requires a designer? (Circle it.) How can you tell?

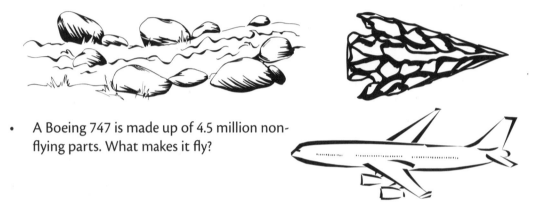

    *   A Boeing 747 is made up of 4.5 million non-flying parts. What makes it fly?

4. During Darwin's time, it was believed that a cell was a relatively simple blob of protoplasm, with a nucleus and a cell wall. It wasn't too farfetched to imagine it forming under primitive earth conditions. Today we have learned that the 'simple' cell is anything but simple.

    On the next page you will find a diagram of a cell. Pretend that it is a giant spaceship that is large enough to cover the city of New York.

    You will be given some cutouts that represent certain key areas of the spaceship community (parts of the cell).

    Paste them in the proper place on the spaceship as they are discussed in class.

Spaceship cell

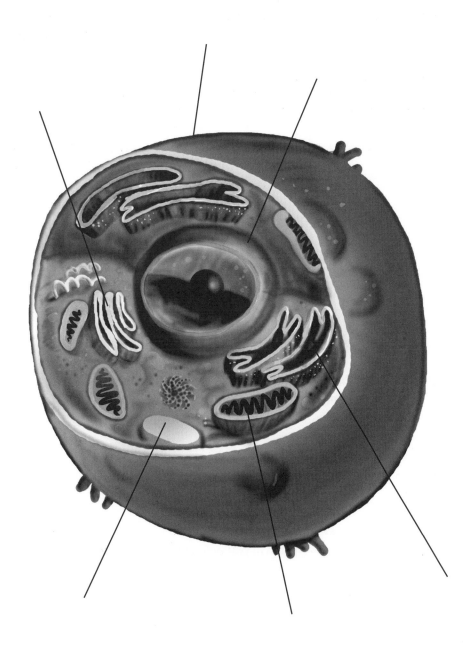

5. Now, let's see what the eyewitness report says about the arrival of life on the earth.

   ✓ **Job 12:7–10** (NIV) 'But ask the animals, and they will teach you, or the birds of the air, and they will tell you; or speak to the earth, and it will teach you, or let the fish of the sea inform you. Which of all these does not know that the hand of the LORD has done this? In his hand is the life of every creature and the breath of all mankind.'

   What is it that the animals, birds, earth and fish will tell you if you ask? (Highlight or underline the part of the passage that tells you the answer.)

   ✓ **Colossians 1:16** (NIV) 'For by him all things were created: things in heaven and on earth, visible and invisible, whether thrones or powers or rulers or authorities; all things were created by him and for him.'

   What does this passage tell us that God created? _____

   _____

   _____

   Would those categories above even include the first living thing? _____

   ✓ **Nehemiah 9:6** (NIV) 'You alone are the LORD. You made the heavens, even the highest heavens, and all their starry host, the earth and all that is on it, the seas and all that is in them. You give life to everything, and the multitudes of heaven worship you.'

   Who was the Intelligent Designer who gave life to all things? Highlight or underline your answer.

6. Is there a difference between the two ways of looking at the origin of life? Which is compelling (convincing)? Which will you believe?

   _____

   _____

7 C's Connection: _____

It All Begins With Genesis — LESSON 18

Recognizing different worldviews in science (part 4)

Life—the many varieties of living things

There are so many different kinds of living things. How did they all come about? Intelligent people disagree. They give two very different ideas. They wear very different pairs of eyeglasses. Where does the truth lie? Could the great differences be a result of presuppositions?

1. Think again about the person who doesn't believe in God, who doesn't believe Scripture is true. If you were that person, how would you explain how a simple cell that 'just happened' from chemical processes could form all the different kinds of life we see on earth today? Give it a try in the space below.

_____

_____

_____

_____

2. The following quote is from *Biology Principles*, Holt, p. 251.

'Scientists have concluded that the great diversity of life on earth is the result of more than 3.5 billion years of evolution, during which species were replaced over time by other species … . Macroevolution refers to change among species over time. The replacement of dinosaurs by mammals is an example of macroevolution.'

Is this anything like the story you came up with above? _____

Does it sound reasonable? _____

What kind of eyeglasses are the writers of this textbook wearing?

_____

3. In class today we'll discuss Charles Darwin and his idea about the various groups of life.

4. We're going to introduce and illustrate for you several 50-cent words. Here are the words:

   ✓ information

   ✓ genetic recombination

   ✓ natural selection

   ✓ mutations

5. *Why* are we studying 'science' in a Bible study? Read the reasons given below and circle the best answer.

   a. We want to be able to 'bug' our science teacher about creation/evolution.

   b. We want to win the arguments about creation/evolution.

   c. We want to have 'proof' that the Bible is true.

   d. We want to know more about God by what He has done in creation.

   Finally and most importantly, let's look at the eyewitness report.

6. In order to check your answer on the previous question, read the following passage from Romans. In it Paul is saying that God is very angry with men who have suppressed (pushed down, ignored) an important truth.

   Romans 1:18–20 (NIV) 'The wrath of God is being revealed from heaven against all the godlessness and wickedness of men who suppress the truth by their wickedness, since what may be known about God is plain to them, because God has made it plain to them. For since the creation of the world God's invisible qualities—his eternal power and divine nature—have been clearly seen, being understood from what has been made, so that men are without excuse.'

✓ What things has God made clear to all mankind about His character?

_____

_____

_____

✓ How have these things about His character been clearly shown to all men?

_____

_____

_____

Can you see now why it is so helpful to study life, DNA, rocks, fossils, etc.? Discuss with your group leader what you have learned about the Creator from studying His creation.

7. Your next assignment is a familiar passage! Read the passage from Genesis 1 below and circle every time 'after their/its kind' is written. Then underline or highlight with a color each 'kind' God gave us.

Genesis 1:20–25 (NIV) 'And God said, "Let the water teem with living creatures, and let birds fly above the earth across the expanse of the sky." So God created the great creatures of the sea and every living and moving thing with which the water teems, according to their kinds, and every winged bird according to its kind. And God saw that it was good. God blessed them and said, "Be fruitful and increase in number and fill the water in the seas, and let the birds increase on the earth." And there was evening, and there was morning—the fifth day. And God said, "Let the land produce living creatures according to their kinds: livestock, creatures that move along the ground, and wild animals, each according to its kind." And it was so. God made the wild animals according to their kinds, the livestock according to their kinds, and all the creatures that move along the ground according to their kinds. And God saw that it was good.'

8. Read the passage from 1 Corinthians written below. In this chapter Paul is talking about the resurrection of the dead, and he is explaining that the resurrection body will not be like the body we now have. Then he goes on to tell us something that is helpful as we look at the Genesis kinds and at man's ideas of evolution. What did you learn from reading this verse? (Does our understanding about DNA agree or disagree with this verse?)

   1 Corinthians 15:39 (NIV) 'All flesh is not the same: men have one kind of flesh, animals have another, birds another and fish another.'

   _____

   _____

   _____

9. Is there a difference between the two ways of looking at the origin of the major groups of life? Whom will you believe?

   _____

   _____

7 C's Connection: _____

Recognizing different worldviews in science (part 5)

Origin of mankind

Now it really gets personal. Where did *you* come from? Up from the slime? Or were you specially created in the image of God? Let's look at the two major worldviews on man's beginnings.

1. A person who does not believe in God or His Word still needs to think about himself—who he is and how he got here. What one believes about his origin will also determine how he will live his life—his purpose. Use your imagination. What would that person reason about how man arrived in this world? Write his explanation below.

    _____

    _____

    _____

2. The following quotations are from *Principles of Biology*, Holt, chapter 14.

    'Primates evolved about 60 million years ago from small, insect-eating mammals that lived in trees.

    ⇩

    'Human ancestors diverged from the evolutionary line leading to gorillas and chimpanzees about 4 million years ago.

    ⇩

    '*Homo habilis*, the first hominid assigned to our own genus, was known to make and use stone tools. It evolved from an australopithecine ancestor about 2 million years ago.

    ⇩

    '*Homo erectus* was the second species of humans to live on earth. It evolved in Africa 1.5 million years ago.

    ⇩

    '*Homo sapiens*, our species, evolved from *Homo erectus* ancestors in Africa about 500,000 years ago.'

3. What kind of worldview glasses is the person who wrote that biology text wearing? Does it sound reasonable, considering his worldview?

   _____

4. In our class today we'll discuss the Biblical explanation for those fossil men and apes. Fill in the blank for each member of the human 'family tree' after the discussion.

	Naturalistic worldview	Biblical worldview
australopithecines		
Homo habilis		
Homo erectus		
Neanderthal		
Homo sapiens		

5. After the discussion, write below one thing that you didn't know about these fossils that you learned today.

   _____

   _____

   _____

6. What does the eyewitness report have to say about the origin of mankind? Of course, you know—you've already studied it. But review is good, so let's look at the creation of man in Genesis one more time.

   Genesis 1:26–27 (NIV) 'Then God said, "Let us make man in our image, in our likeness, and let them rule over the fish of the sea and the birds of the air, over the livestock, over all the earth, and over all the creatures that move along the ground." So God created man in his own image, in the image of God he created him; male and female he created them.'

✓ What Day of Creation did this happen? (If you don't know this already, you'll have to go to your Bible again and read the whole chapter.)

_____

✓ When you read how God created man, how is it different from what was said earlier in the chapter about the creation of animals? (There are at least two things you should notice.)

_____

_____

_____

Genesis 2:7 (NIV) 'The Lord God formed the man from the dust of the ground and breathed into his nostrils the breath of life, and the man became a living being. '

✓ How did God form man?

_____

Genesis 2:21–22 (NIV) 'So the Lord God caused the man to fall into a deep sleep; and while he was sleeping, he took one of the man's ribs and closed up the place with flesh. Then the Lord God made a woman from the rib he had taken out of the man, and he brought her to the man.'

✓ How did God form woman?

_____

✓ Who was formed first, man or woman?

_____

We know these questions are very obvious. We aren't trying to insult your intelligence. But think for a minute about the naturalistic worldview about how man came to be. Are there any clear contradictions between that worldview you hear everywhere and what the Word of God has to say? Discuss these things with your teacher and group.

7. Finally, just in case you've missed it, let's look at two cross-references. There are many more, but we'll go easy on you. (This is to help you see that Genesis is not the only place that talks about man's creation and what it means to be created in the image of God.)

   Psalm 139:13–14 (NIV) 'For you created my inmost being; you knit me together in my mother's womb. I praise you because I am fearfully and wonderfully made; your works are wonderful.'

   ✓ Who created you? How?

   _____

   ✓ When you think about the way God made you, what should it cause you to do in response? (What did the Psalmist do?)

   _____

   _____

   Job 33:4, 6 (NIV) 'The Spirit of God has made me; the breath of the Almighty gives me life. I am just like you before God; I too have been taken from clay.'

   ✓ Who made you and gave you life?

   _____

   ✓ Did you come from an ape-like creature? No? What does this verse say you came from?

   _____

8. Is there a difference between the two ways of looking at the origin of man? Which is more compelling to you? Whom will you believe?

   _____

   _____

7 C's Connection: _____

How did evil come into the world?

Remember what the world was like at the end of Genesis 2? God had created a 'very good' world, and He had created Adam and Eve to live in a beautiful Garden and to be in charge of the wonderful world. There was no death, no sickness and no sorrow.

But that's not the world we find today.

What happened? Is it all about eating a piece of fruit?

Genesis 3 is one of the most important chapters in the whole Bible. We'll be studying it for the next five lessons. So, let's dig in.

1. Today you will be using your observation sheet for Genesis 3. You will need your colored pencils, pens or highlighters today.

2. Read Genesis 3. As you go, mark the following four key words. They are the *who*'s of the chapter. Think about what you are reading when you mark them.

    ✓ Every mention of *Adam* (he, the man). Use the same symbol you used in chapters 1 and 2. (blue stick figure)

    ✓ Every mention of *Eve* (she, the woman). (pink stick figure)

    ✓ Every mention of the LORD *God*. Use the same symbol you used for God in chapter 1. (purple crown)

    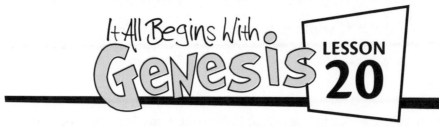

    ✓ Every mention of the *serpent*. (Use a red pitchfork. He didn't have one, of course, but it makes an easy symbol to see and to remember.)

3. As time permits, go through chapter 3 again and answer the questions written in the margin of your observation sheet. This week we just want you to become familiar with what is found in chapter 3.

4. Did you notice how many times words like 'curse,' 'death' and 'dying' were used? Go through chapter 3 and mark these key words. Use black, perhaps drawing a black cloud around the words.

5. Now that you have read through chapter 3 several times, you should be able to answer some simple who, what, where and when questions. See what you have observed by filling in the chart on the next page.

Observation of Genesis 3

Who were the persons talked about in Genesis 3?
Where did the events of Genesis 3 take place?
When did these things happen? (Is a time given? Look at the end of Genesis 2, and see if you can tell how long after creation this happened.)
What events happened in this chapter?
Why is this one of the most important chapters in Scripture?

6. Finally, look at the suggested themes for this chapter that are listed at the end of the observation sheet. Circle the best theme and then draw a picture that will help you remember what happened in Genesis 3.

_____

_____

7 C's Connection: _____

Temptation and sin

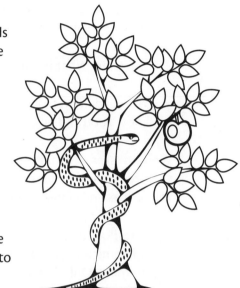

Is it a sin to be tempted? When does sin really happen? Is there a step-by-step process that leads to sin, or is there no warning? Is it 'wham bang,' and before you know it, you've sinned? When does a temptation become a sin? Interesting questions.

1. First of all, read the passage below. It tells you one reason, or purpose, Jesus came. What was that reason? Underline or highlight your answer.

   1 John 3:8 (NIV) 'He who does what is sinful is of the devil, because the devil has been sinning from the beginning. The reason the Son of God appeared was to destroy the devil's work.'

2. Today we need to go back again to Genesis 3 to see what we can learn about temptation. It was there that the first temptation happened, which led to the first sin. We need to see what really happened. It would be helpful to role-play Eve's temptation. One person can play the role of the serpent, and one can play the role of Eve. The rest of the class should listen and observe what is happening.

   Serpent (to the woman): 'Did God really say, "You must not eat from any tree in the Garden"?'

   Question: What is the serpent doing here? Who's word is he questioning?

   _____

   Could he be encouraging Eve to doubt God's Word? Is he distorting it?

   Woman (to the serpent): 'We may eat fruit from the trees in the Garden, but God did say, "You must not eat fruit from the tree that is in the middle of the Garden, and you must not touch it, or you will die." '

   Question: What did Eve add to God's Word here? _____

Did God *really* say she could not touch the fruit? Go back and look at Genesis 2:16–17. What did God really say?

_____

Serpent (to the woman): 'You will not surely die! For God knows that when you eat of it your eyes will be opened, and you will be like God, knowing good and evil.'

Question: What is the serpent doing now? He is a _____.

Yes, in addition to lying, the serpent is telling a half-truth, because she really will know good and evil, and he knows that appeals to her.)

Woman (sees tree and thinks aloud): 'Yum, that tree really looks good to eat! Wow, that tree really is beautiful; I love to look at it. Hmmm, so it really will make me wise? I will be like God Himself. Now, that sounds wise to me.'

Question: There were three things that tempted Eve. These three things are the same things that tempt us today, and we'll look at them more closely in a moment. Only one question for now. Has Eve sinned yet?

_____

Woman (takes fruit off tree and eats; her husband with her eats also.)

Question: Has Eve sinned yet? _____ Has Adam?_____

Here's an interesting question: was Adam with Eve the whole time she was being tempted by the serpent? He isn't mentioned until she eats, and then he is said to be there. If he was with her, it is strange that the serpent talked only to her and that Adam did nothing to help. It is possible the serpent was tempting Eve over a longer period of time. The text doesn't say how long this temptation went on. Perhaps she was alone most of the time, but he was with her when she finally gave in to the temptation. We don't really know, but it is worth thinking about.

3. What is a temptation? Is it the same as a sin? Is it a sin to be tempted? What is the difference between a sin and a temptation? These are important questions.

✓ The Hebrew word for temptation is *nasah*. It means 'a test, an attempt to prove the quality of something, to put to the test.' It can also be defined as a 'squeezing.' For example, your mother may give you $20 and ask you to go to the store to buy some groceries for her. Could she be testing you to see if you will handle the money responsibly?

✓ Another example: In school, you are given a very hard math exam to take. You are sitting next to the smartest girl in the school. The teacher leaves the room while the exam is going on. What is being tried, or proven, here? If you handle these situations well, what will you have proven to your mother or to the teacher?

_____

_____

4. Now, what is a sin?

✓ One Hebrew word for sin is *chata*. It means 'to miss the mark, go wrong.' If your parents ask you to go to the store for groceries, you sin if you disobey their instructions and buy $20 worth of candy. That is missing the mark of what is expected of you.

In the example of taking the math test in school, sin occurs if you copy answers from the girl's paper. You miss the mark when honesty is expected of you and you are dishonest.

✓ The Bible gives us some good definitions of sin. In the verses listed below, underline or highlight the part of the verse that tells us what sin means.

Isaiah 53:6 (NAS) 'All of us like sheep have gone astray, each of us has turned to his own way.'

Romans 14:23 (NAS) 'But he who doubts is condemned if he eats, because [his eating is] not from faith; and whatever is not from faith is sin.'

James 4:17 (NAS) 'Therefore, to one who knows [the] right thing to do, and does not do it, to him it is sin.'

1 John 3:4 (NAS) 'Everyone who practices sin also practices lawlessness; and sin is lawlessness.'

Okay, we know what sin and temptation are, and how Eve was tempted. Now we need to get really practical and see how it works in our lives. Pray that the Holy Spirit would help you see the way that you are tempted to sin in your own life.

5. Temptation usually falls into one of three different varieties. 1 John 2:16 explains this to us:

    1 John 2:16 (NIV) 'For everything in the world—the cravings of sinful man, the lust of his eyes and the boasting of what he has and does—comes not from the Father but from the world.'

    ✓ List the three different temptations that are in the world.

    a. _____

    b. _____

    c. _____

6. Do you understand what each of the three temptations above means? Let's see if we can make it clearer for you.

    a. The 'cravings of sinful man' (also called 'lust of the flesh' in some translations) describe sinful things that make us feel good. They include eating too much or being lazy.

    b. 'Lust of the eyes' refers to things that seem beautiful to us. We just must have them ... right away! They include beautiful jewels, fancy homes, boats, clothes, cars, CDs, video games or anything we just want to own or possess.

    c. 'Boasting of what he has and does' (called 'pride of life' in other translations) would include things that make us feel smart and important, better than other people.

    ✓ When Eve 'saw that the tree was good for food,' which of the three temptations

       listed above was she experiencing?_____

    ✓ When Eve 'saw that the tree was a delight to the eyes,' which of the above

       temptations was she experiencing?_____

    ✓ When Eve 'saw that the tree was desirable to make one wise,' which of the above

       temptations was she experiencing? _____

7. Let's see if you can identify which type of temptation is happening in the each of the following everyday situations. If it is the 'cravings of sinful man,' put a **1** beside the description. If it is 'lust of the eyes,' put **2** beside it. If it is 'pride of life,' put **3** beside it.

_____ You really want to get an A on that math test, because you will win the prize and everyone will think you are smart.

_____ That is the most beautiful doll (or bicycle, or painting or jewelry) you have ever seen. You want it for your own. You really, really want it.

_____ You know that movie is R-rated, but you still want to see it.

_____ You are jealous of Sam because people seem to like him better than you. If you lie 'just a little,' maybe they will like you better.

_____ You know that certain Web sites on the Internet are not pleasing to the Lord, but it makes you feel good to go to them anyway.

_____ You are full after a big dinner, and you have been gaining some weight lately, but that third chocolate brownie just looks too good.

_____ If you could only have a new Nintendo® system, you would be so happy.

_____ On Saturday, there are many things you should or could be doing with your time off from school. Your dad asks you to help him in the yard that morning. But you sleep till noon instead.

8. Here's another question for you. How do you go from a temptation to a sin? Is there a progression that we can observe, as a temptation finally turns into a sin? Let's look at James 1:13–15 to see if we can answer that question.

James 1:13–15 (NIV) 'When tempted, no one should say, "God is tempting me." For God cannot be tempted by evil, nor does he tempt anyone; but each one is tempted when, by his own evil desire [lust], he is dragged away and enticed. Then, after desire has conceived, it gives birth to sin; and sin, when it is full-grown, gives birth to death.'

✓ Does God tempt us to do evil? Circle: yes or no

✓ What comes first? (verse 14) _____

✓ Do you know what 'lust' is? Lust is excessive desire, especially to meet one's physical needs. When you are 'enticed,' that means you really want something and you are tempted by it. What happens next, after that lust has taken control?

_____

_____

✓ Once sin is born, what happens?

_____

_____

9. In the space below, see if you can draw what temptation is and when the temptation becomes sin (which results in death). Use these drawings as the principle players in your scene. Draw (1) when everything is fine (2) when temptation is occurring and (3) when temptation is yielded to and sin occurs. (Of course, this is just an analogy. Fish don't really sin!)

1.	2.	3.

Now let's take our fish and bait analogy one step further. How might the fish have avoided temptation? That is really the question for us. What is a Christian to do when he is tempted? Temptation is a reality. Sin is a choice. The secret is to learn what God's Word tells us about temptation and sin so we won't yield to temptation.

10. Read the verses below and answer the questions after each verse.

Hebrews 4:14–16 (NIV) 'Therefore, since we have a great high priest who has gone through the heavens, Jesus the Son of God, let us hold firmly to the faith we profess. For we do not have a high priest who is unable to sympathize with our weaknesses, but we have one who has been tempted in every way, just as we are—yet was without sin. Let us then approach the throne of grace with confidence, so that we may receive mercy and find grace to help us in our time of need.'

✓ Who is our High Priest? (verse 14) _____

✓ In verse 15 we learn something about Jesus and temptation. Record what you learn below.

_____

_____

✓ Because of what happened in verse 15, we are given a command with a promise in verse 16. This should help us when we are tempted.

_____

_____

Matthew 26:41 (NIV) 'Watch and pray so that you will not fall into temptation. The spirit is willing, but the body is weak.'

✓ *What* command is listed here to help you?

_____

Matthew 6:9, 13 (NIV) 'This, then, is how you should pray: "Our Father in heaven, hallowed be your name, ... and lead us not into temptation, but deliver us from the evil one."'

✓ *What* should we pray to the Father?

_____

_____

1 Corinthians 10:12–13 (NIV) 'So, if you think you are standing firm, be careful that you don't fall! No temptation has seized you except what is common to man. And God is faithful; he will not let you be tempted beyond what you can bear. But when you are tempted, he will also provide a way out so that you can stand up under it.'

✓ Put verse 12 in your own words. What warning is God giving us?

_____

_____

✓ Verse 13 tells us that being tempted is a common thing to man. Then the verse includes a promise. Write the promise in your own words.

_____

_____

_____

Philippians 4:8 (NIV) 'Finally, brothers, whatever is true, whatever is noble, whatever is right, whatever is pure, whatever is lovely, whatever is admirable—if anything is excellent or praiseworthy—think about such things.'

✓ When you are tempted and struggling with wrong thoughts, what are you told to think about? Write it in your own words.

_____

_____

_____

_____

When you are tempted, take every thought captive …
And Philippians 4:8 it!

7 C's Connection: _____

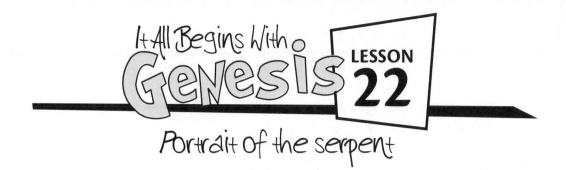

It All Begins With Genesis
LESSON 22
Portrait of the serpent

Can we say 'the devil made me do it'? Who is the devil, anyway? Is he a man in red pajamas with a pitchfork? Is he the talking snake of Genesis 3? We called him the devil, but it doesn't say who he is in Genesis 3, does it? How can we find more about him?

In this lesson we are going to be learning another skill of inductive Bible study. We are going to do a character study ... on 'the tempter.' When you do a character study, you look in a concordance or use Bible-study software to find all of the Bible references to the person you want to study. Then you look up the references. Next you need to see what questions are answered by the various texts, and finally you make a summary in an outline or chart form. We don't have time here to check on all the references to the 'evil one' in Scripture, but we will look at some of the most helpful, and from those you will make a portrait—a word picture—of this serpent.

1. We begin with Genesis, of course. You will need your observation sheet for chapter 3. On it you drew 'pitchforks' every time you saw the word serpent. Now let's see what you learn by going back to your markings.

   ✓ *How* is the serpent described in 3:1?

   _____

   ✓ Look at verse 3:4. When he said to the woman, 'You surely shall not die!' *what* was the serpent doing?

   _____

   ✓ That's right, he lied! And in 3:13 we learn that the serpent did what else?

   _____

   _____

✓ The Lᴏʀᴅ God cursed the serpent. Fill in the blanks below so you can remember the curse (verses 14–15):

'On your _____ you shall go, and _____ shall you eat all the days of your life. I will put _____ between you and the woman, and between your seed and her _____. ['Enmity' means hostility, bad feelings.]

In verse 15, 'seed' means 'descendents,' and the woman's seed is Christ. (We'll study this more at a later time.) So what does God say about Christ and about the seed of the serpent?

'He [Christ] shall bruise you _____ , and you shall

bruise him on the _____.'

This is a very exciting verse because it is the first time in the Bible that the Gospel is mentioned, even though it may be difficult for us to understand.

2. We have made a chart for you to fill in at the end of this lesson, and we have included some of the Scriptures that tell you more about the serpent. As you read what the Bible tells us about the serpent, you can complete the chart. When you finish, you will have a word picture of who the serpent is and what he is like and what he does. You'll then be able to see the information all in one place, and that should help you to remember it better.

Pray as you continue to learn more about the evil one. He doesn't want people to know what he is up to, so it is important to ask for the Lord's wisdom and protection as you work.

✓ Begin your chart by looking at what you learned in the beginning of this lesson about the serpent from Genesis 3. First, you read what he was called (serpent). You can write the answer under 'What is he called?' on your chart. (We have already done this for you so you can see how to get started.)

You also learned something about his character (what he is like) from 3:1. He is 'crafty.' You then write your observation in the column 'What is he like?'

Another thing we learn is what he does for a living (see verse 13). He 'deceives.' That should be written in the column 'What does he do?'

Do you have the idea? Let's see what you can do by yourself in the passages that follow.

✓ Read the following passage. Mark or highlight in red or pink the names for the serpent given there. There should be four names. Then write what you learned under the heading 'What is he called?' on your portrait chart.

Revelation 20:1–3 (NIV) 'And I saw an angel coming down out of heaven, having the key to the Abyss and holding in his hand a great chain. He seized the dragon, that ancient serpent, who is the devil, or Satan, and bound him for a thousand years. He threw him into the Abyss, and locked and sealed it over him, to keep him from deceiving the nations any more until the thousand years were ended. After that, he must be set free for a short time.'

✓ Now read the following passage. Chapter 12 of Revelation tells us many things, but for our purposes now, you need to see only two things. First, underline or highlight in red or pink who the devil is. Write his names under the 'What is he called?' heading in your chart. Second, this chapter tells you something about what the devil does. Underline or highlight that in blue, and transfer it to the chart under the heading 'What does he do?'

Revelation 12:7–9 (NIV) 'And there was war in heaven. Michael and his angels fought against the dragon, and the dragon and his angels fought back. But he was not strong enough, and they lost their place in heaven. The great dragon was hurled down—that ancient serpent called the devil, or Satan, who leads the whole world astray. He was hurled to the earth, and his angels with him.'

✓ Revelation 12:12, 17 has some important things to tell us as well. In verse 12 we learn something more about what he is like. This tells us something about his character, his personality. Highlight or underline the appropriate words or phrases in yellow, and write them under 'What is he like?' on your portrait chart. In verse 17 we learn what the evil one does. You should mark what he does in blue, remember? Then transfer the words to 'What does he do?' on your chart.

Revelation 12:12, 17 (NIV) 'Therefore rejoice, you heavens and you who dwell in them! But woe to the earth and the sea, because the devil has gone down to you! He is filled with fury, because he knows that his time is short. ... Then the dragon was enraged at the woman and went off to make war against the rest of her offspring—those who obey God's commandments and hold to the testimony of Jesus.'

✓ In the passage written below, Jesus is talking to unbelieving Pharisees. In it we learn something about the character of the evil one. Underline or highlight what you learn in yellow and write it under 'What is he like?' on your chart.

John 8:44 (NIV) 'You belong to your father, the devil, and you want to carry out your father's desire. He was a murderer from the beginning, not holding to the truth, for there is no truth in him. When he lies, he speaks his native language, for he is a liar and the father of lies.'

✓ The next passage tells us what Christ has done for us, and it also tells us something about the power that the devil has. Mark what power the devil has in blue, and write it under 'What does he do?' on your chart.

Hebrews 2:14–15 (NIV) 'Since the children have flesh and blood, he too shared in their humanity so that by his death he might destroy him who holds the power of death—that is, the devil—and free those who all their lives were held in slavery by their fear of death.'

✓ This next passage tells us more about 'What does he do?' Highlight what he does in blue and transfer it to your chart.

1 John 5:19 (NIV) 'We know that we are children of God, and that the whole world is under the control of the evil one.'

✓ The next passage talks about forgiveness, but it also tells us something about what Satan is like. Mark what he is like in yellow and transfer it to 'What is he like?' on your portrait chart.

2 Corinthians 2:10–11 (NIV) 'If you forgive anyone, I also forgive him. And what I have forgiven—if there was anything to forgive—I have forgiven in the sight of Christ for your sake, in order that Satan might not outwit us. For we are not unaware of his schemes.'

✓ In this next passage, we see the evil one referred to as 'the god of this world.' It tells us something else about what he does in this verse. Please highlight this in blue and include it in 'What does he do?' on your chart.

2 Corinthians 4:3–4 (NIV) 'And even if our gospel is veiled, it is veiled to those who are perishing. The god of this age has blinded the minds of unbelievers, so that they cannot see the light of the gospel of the glory of Christ, who is the image of God.'

✓ The next passage warns us to watch out for those who serve the evil one, because of something that Satan does. Highlight this in blue and write it under 'What does he do?' on your chart.

2 Corinthians 11:14–15 (NIV) 'And no wonder, for Satan himself masquerades as an angel of light. It is not surprising, then, if his servants masquerade as servants of righteousness. Their end will be what their actions deserve.'

✓ This next passage gives us two more names by which the devil is called. Highlight and mark these in pink and write them on your chart under 'What is he called?'

Ephesians 2:1–2 (NIV) 'As for you, you were dead in your transgressions and sins, in which you used to live when you followed the ways of this world and of the ruler of the kingdom of the air, the spirit who is now at work in those who are disobedient.'

✓ This last passage gives us a command to obey because of something the evil one does. It also gives us another name by which he can be called. See if you can find and record 'What does he do?' and 'What is he called?'

1 Peter 5:8 (NIV) 'Be self-controlled and alert. Your enemy the devil prowls around like a roaring lion looking for someone to devour.'

7 C's Connection: _____

Portrait of the Serpent

	What is he called?	What is he like?	What does he do?
Genesis 3:1	serpent	crafty	
Genesis 3:13			deceives
Revelation 20:1–3			
Revelation 12:7–9			
Revelation 12:12, 17			
John 8:44			
Hebrews 2:14–15			
1 John 5:19			
2 Corinthians 2:10–11			
2 Corinthians 4:3–4			
2 Corinthians 11:14–15			
Ephesians 2:1–2			
1 Peter 5:8			

It All Begins With Genesis

The fallen world

We live in a fallen world. Just what does that mean? Did the created world itself change because of Adam's sin? Was it just a matter of people eventually dying, or was it more than that? We really need to know how the Fall of mankind affected the whole cosmos! Only then can we understand what a great God we have.

1. Well, the deceiver succeeded. The forbidden fruit was eaten. Where does that leave man? We can tell a lot by the things Adam and Eve did and said after they sinned in the Garden. It tells us about what happens when we sin, also.

    Take out your observation worksheet for Genesis 3, and let's talk about verses 7–14. Our purpose today is to see just how much God's perfect world changed after the sin of Adam and Eve.

    ✓ Genesis 3:7. The first thing Adam and Eve did after they sinned was to find fig leaves and make coverings for themselves. *What* feeling were they experiencing for the first time that led to their covering themselves?

    _____

    ✓ Is that why you think we wear clothes today? _____

    ✓ Verses 8–10. God walked in the Garden regularly with Adam and Eve, it seems, but this time they hid. *What* kind of feeling did they have for the first time, which caused them to hide?

    _____

    ✓ Think of a time when you have sinned. Did you hide? What are some of the things you do to hide when you know you have sinned and you are afraid?

    _____

    _____

✓ Verses 11–12. When God confronts Adam and asks him to confess that he has sinned, does he confess? Absolutely not! *What* does he do?

_____

_____

✓ Isn't it interesting that Adam looked for someone to blame? He blamed not only his wife, but he seems to blame God as well, because God gave him his wife! Think for a moment about a time when you sinned and were caught. Whom did you blame? Is this something you do often, too? (We all look for someone to blame.)

_____

_____

✓ In verses 13–14, Eve does the same thing. Whom does she blame?

_____

✓ 'The devil made me do it!' Can you think of a time when you, or someone you know, blamed something they did on the evil one? (Yes, the evil one is busy encouraging us to sin, but remember what we learned about sin being a choice?)

_____

_____

_____

_____

_____

_____

✓ There is one more thing about this passage that we would like you to see. Have you ever wondered why God called out to Adam and asked him, 'Where are you?' God knows everything; He certainly didn't need to ask. And do you suppose that God really didn't know that Adam had eaten from the tree? Did He have to ask Adam? Can you think of a reason God had for asking questions when He obviously didn't need to know the answers?

_____

_____

_____

Do you suppose God was giving Adam the chance to confess his sin? How much better it is when we are honest about our sin and we confess it, both to God and to the one we have sinned against. In fact, God tells us that because of Christ, we are forgiven and cleansed of sin when we simply confess it (1 John 1:9).

2. Well, it was a wonderful world that God created—but something happened to change all that, and you know from our past two weeks of study that it was the sin of Adam that brought about so many changes. Now we are going to look at how things changed after the Fall. Refer again to your observation worksheet on Genesis 3 as you answer these questions.

✓ *What* came into the world as a result of the Fall, discussed in Genesis 3:10? (You studied this already, but we need to remember it.)

_____

✓ *What* did God tell Eve about pain and about her relationship with her husband, Adam, after their sin? Look at Genesis 3:16. There are two different things that she learned would happen. List them below.

_____

_____

✓ *What* happened to the ground of the earth as a result of Adam's sin (Genesis 3:17)?

_____

✓ Also in Genesis 3:17–19, we learn how work changed after the Fall. *What* would Adam's work be like after the Fall?

_____

_____

✓ *What* did God tell Adam was going to happen to him eventually (Genesis 3:19)?

_____

You will find a chart located at the end of this lesson. It is titled 'When sin came into the world…'. On this chart you will draw a word picture (or if you are artistic, a real drawing) of the many things that came into the world following Adam's sin. To begin your chart, go back to the questions you completed on the first three pages of this lesson. Based on your study of Genesis 3, write or draw on the chart what entered the world. (For example, you noted that 'shame' was a first result of sin. Write that somewhere on the chart. Now, what else can you add to the picture of life after sin?)

3. Now let's look at an important passage from the New Testament that talks about what happened in Genesis 3. Read the passage below and draw a circle around every mention of 'the creation,' including its synonyms. Then answer the Five W's and H questions that follow.

Romans 8:20–22 (NIV) [20] 'For the creation was subjected to frustration, not by its own choice, but by the will of the one who subjected it, in hope [21] that the creation itself will be liberated from its bondage to decay and brought into the glorious freedom of the children of God. [22] We know that the whole creation has been groaning as in the pains of childbirth right up to the present time.' ('Decay' means 'corruption, spoiling, rottenness.')

✓ *What* happened to the creation in verse 20?

_____

_____

✓ *How* did the creation get that way? Did it subject itself, or if not, who is the one who subjected it? (verse 20)

_____

_____

✓ According to verse 21, the one who subjected the creation to this frustration hopes that the creation will be freed from its bondage (slavery) to *what*? (Note: In Biblical language, the word 'hope' doesn't mean 'maybe'—it means 'a sure thing.')

_____

_____

✓ *What* is the creation doing in verse 22? _____

✓ *When* do you think this 'groaning' and 'decay' began? (Remember, when the world was created, God called it 'very good.')

_____

_____

✓ *When* do you think this groaning and decay will end? _____

_____

✓ Verse 22 talks about the pains of childbirth. When childbirth takes place, the mother has something new and wonderful to look forward to. In the case of the creation, do you have any idea what we can look forward to? Do you know what Scripture promises us is going to happen?

_____

_____

✓ *What* are some examples you can think of that illustrate the groaning and decay of the creation? Transfer these ideas to your word picture chart at the back of the lesson.

4. The passage below describes a person who is lost in sin. This passage gives us some good descriptions of life after sin came into the world. Circle all the personal pronouns (you, us, our, we) that describe the lost person. Then answer the questions that follow.

Ephesians 2:1–3 (NIV) [1]'As for you, you were dead in your transgressions and sins, [2] in which you used to live when you followed the ways of this world and of the ruler of the kingdom of the air, the spirit who is now at work in those who are disobedient. [3] All of us also lived among them at one time, gratifying the cravings of our flesh and following its desires and thoughts. Like the rest, we were by nature objects of wrath.'

✓ *What* is the condition of the person who does not have Christ? (verse 1)

_____

✓ *What* and *who* did this dead person follow? (verse 2) _____

_____

_____

_____

✓ *How* are those who follow the things of verse 2 described? _____

✓ In verse 3, these people do *what* with regards to the flesh?

_____

_____

✓ These dead people of verse 3 are described as children of _____.

Transfer these ideas from Ephesians—about life after sin came into the world—to your chart at the back of this lesson.

Wow, this is all pretty depressing, isn't it? Is there any help, any hope for all this mess? Stay tuned for next week! (Now you know why the Gospel is called 'Good News'!)

7 C's Connection: _____

When sin came into the world ...

It All Begins With Genesis

God's solution

What then? Is it all over for man? Finally, we will see God's solution to the problem. In this lesson we're going to look at three examples of God's love and mercy for fallen man, all found in Genesis 3.

Example #1—the protoevangelium

Genesis 3:15 is a very special verse. It is known as the 'protoevangelium.' (Wow, another 50-cent word. You can impress some people if you know that word!) The prefix 'proto-' means 'first,' and 'evangelium' means 'Good News' or 'Gospel.' This verse is the first time in the Bible that God gives us a 'hint' of the future coming of His Son to save us from our sins. It is exciting that He tells this Good News to Adam and Eve even before He tells them the punishment for their sin. We have printed this verse below, so we can study it better.

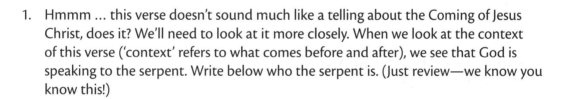

'And I will put enmity between you and the woman, and between your seed and her seed; he shall bruise you on the head, and you shall bruise him on the heel' (NAS).

1. Hmmm … this verse doesn't sound much like a telling about the Coming of Jesus Christ, does it? We'll need to look at it more closely. When we look at the context of this verse ('context' refers to what comes before and after), we see that God is speaking to the serpent. Write below who the serpent is. (Just review—we know you know this!)

_____

2. Let's look at the meaning of several of the words to see what God is saying here.

   The word 'enmity' means 'hatred.'
   The word 'seed' means 'child' or 'offspring.' (For example, I am the seed of my father.)
   The word 'bruise' means 'to crush.'

   The woman here is believed to be Israel, and the seed is of course Christ, who would come from Israel.

3. **Genesis 3:15** says, 'He shall bruise you on the head, and you shall bruise him on the heel.' Now, this is really exciting! There is only one form of death that bruises a person's heel. Do you know what it is?

_____

Now, that is really something! Death by crucifixion wasn't even 'invented' when Genesis 3:15 was written. Yet God said way back in Genesis 3:15 that it would happen to Christ!

4. What does the verse say He (Christ) will do to the serpent's seed? Good news?

_____

5. Now that you understand the definitions and what the verse means, reword Genesis 3:15 in a way that you might explain it to someone who has never studied this verse.

_____

_____

_____

_____

OR

Draw a picture in the circle below showing how you think Genesis 3:15 would look. (You can use stick figures.)

Isn't it exciting? Before Adam and Eve began to have children, God made a way for them to be saved from the sin that had entered the world. He even told Adam and Eve what the way was!

Have you come to Jesus and asked Him to be your Lord? Have you let Him save you from your sin, from living your life your way?

Example #2—God's covering

6. In **Genesis 3:7** we read that after their sin, Adam's and Eve's 'eyes were opened and they knew that they were naked and they sewed fig leaves together and made themselves loin coverings' (NAS). If it weren't so sad, it would be funny to see them scrambling around gathering fragile leaves trying to make clothes!

    Now, look at what God does for Adam and Eve in **Genesis 3:21.** Write it below.

    _____

    _____

7. We already saw that sin makes people ashamed and they want to hide. Clothing is the result of our sin and our need to have a covering for the shame.

    In **Genesis 3:21,** what does God use to make clothing for Adam and Eve?

    _____

8. What did God have to do in order to make those clothes? What had to happen in the world, where it had never happened before?

    _____

9. Read the verse written below and underline in red what the verse says is in the blood.

    Leviticus 17:11 (NAS) 'For the life of the flesh is in the blood, and I have given it to you on the altar to make atonement for your souls; for it is the blood by reason of the life that makes atonement.'

10. *What* does the blood do?

    _____

    'Atonement' means, in the Hebrew, 'to cover, to pardon.' Can you see what a beautiful 'picture' God gave us, all the way back in the Book of Genesis, to show how blood can atone for, or 'cover,' our sins? Can you see that this is just what Jesus' blood did for us?

Example #3—expulsion from the Garden

Now we want you to look at Genesis 3:22–24. It is written below. Mark all references to God in this passage.

> **Genesis 3:22–24** (NAS) 'Then the LORD God said, "Behold, the man has become like one of us, knowing good and evil; and now, lest he stretch out his hand, and take also from the tree of life, and eat, and live forever"—therefore the Lord God sent him out from the garden of Eden, to cultivate the ground from which he was taken. So he drove the man out; and at the east of the garden of Eden he stationed the cherubim, and the flaming sword which turned every direction, to guard the way to the tree of life.'

11. It sounds kind of mean for God to send Adam and Eve out of the Garden, and even place cherubim with a flaming sword to keep them out! But why did God do it? Read the verses and see if you can tell. Write the reason below.

_____

_____

_____

12. What would be so bad about Adam and Eve eating from the Tree of Life in the Garden?

_____

_____

If your answer was: Adam and Eve would have then spent eternity under the Curse, separated from God, and would have no hope of salvation—you are right! God showed His mercy by not letting them live forever as lost people.

13. Let's close with the following important verse from the New Testament. Underline why Jesus came.

    Luke 19:10 (NAS) 'For the Son of Man has come to seek and to save that which was lost.'

Remember the worldview eyeglasses? Now that we have studied the Fall of mankind, we need to look at the way each worldview would answer the question 'What is the reason for death, sorrow and suffering in the world?'

14. How would a person who has a naturalistic worldview (no God, no truth, Scripture is myth) answer that question? Give it a try.

_____

_____

_____

_____

15. Now, put on your biblical eyeglasses and answer the same question. Use quotations from Scripture if you can.

_____

_____

_____

_____

_____

_____

_____

7 C's Connection: _____

Life in the fallen world: Cain and Abel

This week we will study Genesis 4. In this chapter we begin to see what life was like after Adam and Eve sinned. Wow, what a change from the world God created!

And we'll look at how we are to worship and serve God: His way or ours?

1. Today we will need to begin with your observation sheet for Genesis 4. As you have done with the other chapters of Genesis, answer the who, what, where questions found in the margin. This is just a way that will help you to know what happened in the chapter. For now, read and answer questions only for verses 1–16.

2. Have you ever stopped to realize that we have basically two choices when we set about to do something?

    We can do things God's way. ☺
    OR
    We can do things that go against God's way. ☹

God has told us in His Word which way is His way.

In the situations below, mark with a smiley face those actions that are God's way, and mark with a frown those that go against His way:

____ You went to church on Sunday morning and sang joyfully the songs, and you praised God for how great He is.

____ You behaved very badly in Sunday school and refused to listen to the lesson. You wouldn't sit next to a boy you don't like.

____ You didn't clean up your room when your mother asked you to. You were rude when she spoke to you.

____ You were jealous when a girl you know got an A on a paper she wrote, while you got a C on your paper. You said the teacher was unfair.

____ You were so happy for your friend because he was given a beautiful new bicycle for his birthday. It is just like the bicycle you've always wanted.

____ You listened with respect to your father when he corrected you about something last night.

Was it hard to tell which of those things God likes and which He doesn't? Of course not! We know from His Word that we are to worship God. He also tells us to love and treat others as we would wish to be treated. He also tells us to honor and obey our parents. He tells us to rejoice when others rejoice and not to be jealous of them.

Cain and Abel come to God

3. Now we are going to look at two brothers, Cain and Abel, to see how they came to God. You will need to have your observation worksheet for Genesis 4 beside you now so you can answer the questions about Cain and Abel. Begin by reading again verses 1–8. You have already marked Cain and Abel, so it should be easy to spot what you need to know about them. (Notice that these are 'who, what, where' kinds of questions.)

✓ *Who* were the parents of Cain and Abel (verse 1)?

_____

✓ *What* were the occupations of Cain and Abel (their work in the world)?

Abel was _____ .

Cain was _____ .

✓ Both brothers brought offerings to the Lord. List below *what* each brother brought.

_____

✓ *What* did the Lord think about each brother's offering?

_____

_____

_____

   ✓ *How* did Cain react when he saw that God liked Abel's offering but not Cain's offering? (Do you know what 'countenance' means? It means the look on your face—happy, sad, afraid, mad.) What did Cain do next (verses 5, 8)?

_____

_____

_____

4. Cain got mad and he was jealous of his brother. The first thing we need to see is the reason God didn't like Cain's offering. Was God being unfair? Does God like bloody meat but not things that grow from the ground? Does He favor shepherds over farmers? Let's look to Scripture for the answers.

   ✓ Had God told them in the past about the kind of offering they should bring to Him? The offerings people needed to bring to God in those days after Adam's Fall were sin offerings. When they brought offerings to God, they were asking for forgiveness for their sins. Cain and Abel were both sinners who needed forgiveness. Let's look at the passage printed below to find out how sins were forgiven. Use your highlighter or pen to underline how sins were forgiven.

   Hebrews 9:22 (NIV) 'In fact, the law requires that nearly everything be cleansed with blood, and without the shedding of blood there is no forgiveness.'

You just learned that without blood being shed, sin couldn't be forgiven. Do you remember when we studied about Adam's and Eve's sin? One of the things we learned was that God had to kill animals in order for Adam and Eve to have skins to cover them.

What happened when God killed the animals? Right! Blood was shed to cover the sin.

   ✓ So, from the Scripture above, what was a reason that Cain's offering was an unacceptable way to seek forgiveness?

_____

_____

_____

   ✓ God's Word gives us another reason that Cain's offering

was unacceptable. It is found in the verse printed below. Color or mark the word (mentioned three times) that explains why Abel's offering was better than Cain's.

Hebrews 11:4 (NIV) 'By faith Abel offered God a better sacrifice than Cain did. By faith he was commended as a righteous man, when God spoke well of his offerings. And by faith he still speaks, even though he is dead.'

Do you know what it means to have faith? It means that Abel believed God, even when he couldn't see it for himself. God had taught Adam and Eve from the time of their sin that there was a way to have forgiveness for sins, and that it was through a blood offering. Abel was faithful to obey God's way for coming to Him. Cain was not.

✓ Cain and Abel were told that they would have forgiveness through the shedding of blood, the blood of a very special animal prepared the way God had taught them. Today we have forgiveness of sins through the shedding of blood. Whose blood was given as our sacrifice for sins?

_____

✓ Can you think of ways you are sometimes like Cain and sometimes like Abel when you come to God? Like Cain, do you sometimes follow your own rules, your own way? Do you get angry when things don't go well, even when you haven't obeyed? Do you become jealous of others who have been obedient, even when you haven't? Or, like Abel, do you trust in God's promises about Jesus? Do you really seek to know God through His Word? Think about it, and write an example of how you sometimes 'do it your way' like Cain.

_____

_____

_____

_____

God confronts Cain

God warned Cain about sin and its consequences in verse 7, but Cain ignored the warning and killed his brother. What happened next? Now we need to look at the verses that show how God deals with Cain (verses 9–16). Let's put on a play. If you are doing this study with a class, ask someone to play the part of God and someone else to play the part of Cain. Other members of the class can answer the questions. Or, you can do the role-playing with your own parent or sibling and answer the questions together. Ready, let's go!

(Scene: Cain and Abel are out in the field. Cain murders Abel. Cain has rejected God's clear warning.)

God: 'Where is Abel your brother?'

Cain: 'I don't know. Am I my brother's keeper?'

Question for discussion: God is seeking out Cain just like he sought out Adam after Adam sinned. Why do you suppose God does that?

_____

_____

Why do you suppose Cain answers the way he does? What is he doing by answering that way?

_____

_____

_____

_____

God: 'What have you done? Listen! Your brother's blood cries out to me from the ground. Now you are under a curse and driven from the ground, which opened its mouth to receive your brother's blood from your hand.

'When you work the ground, it will no longer yield its crops for you. You will be a restless wanderer on the earth.'

Cain: 'My punishment is more than I can bear. Today you are driving me from the land, and I will be hidden from your presence; I will be a restless wanderer on the earth, and whoever finds me will kill me.'

God: 'Not so. If anyone kills Cain, he will suffer vengeance seven times over.' (Then the LORD put a mark on Cain so that nobody who found him would kill him.)

Question: After Cain avoided the chance to confess his sin, and after he hid from his problem by both lying and avoiding the issue, God then cursed him. How does this curse remind you of God's Curse after Adam's sin? (If you have forgotten, go back and look in Genesis 3:17–18.)

_____

_____

Question: Do you see any sign of sorrow or sadness in Cain about his sin? What *do* you see in Cain's behavior?)

_____

_____

Question: Even though Cain was full of self-pity and did not even repent of his sin, God showed mercy on Cain. What are some things you learn about God from the way He deals with Cain? Was God too hard on Cain? Too easy?

_____

_____

_____

Question: Do you have any idea what the 'mark' was that God put on Cain? (Scripture doesn't really tell us, does it?)

The final scene shows Cain going out from the presence of Jehovah, dwelling in the land of Nod, east of Eden.

Question: God was so merciful with Cain. God is a just God, so He had to punish Cain. But He saved his life and prevented anyone from taking vengeance on him. He still gave him the opportunity to turn to Him in the future. God sent Cain out from the presence of Jehovah God. What is so sad about the previous statement? Why is this a terrible punishment?

_____

_____

_____

_____

7 C's Connection: _____

GOD

It All Begins With Genesis

Life in the fallen world: Adam's descendants

Do family 'trees' bore you? In Genesis 4 and 5 we see lots of 'begats.' At first glimpse, all those strange names and lists seem pretty uninteresting.

But God tells us *all* Scripture is important.

And sure enough, there is a lot we can learn from these chapters. They tell us about an important time in history. Sin is growing and flourishing in the land. Is there any way to stop it?

The line of Cain

1. Turn now to the observation sheet you began on Genesis 4. Read verses 17–26. Don't fill in the questions in the margins at this time. We'll cover the answers to those questions in this lesson.

2. We see in **Genesis 4:17** that Cain was married and gave birth to a son named Enoch. Hmmm. Where did Cain get his wife? Since Cain was Eve's son and then Abel, whom would he marry? Some people ask this question in order to ridicule the Bible. Actually, the answer is simple and is found in **Genesis 5:4.** Look on your observation sheet for chapter 5 and see if you can answer the question about Cain's wife.

   _____

   _____

3. Now let's see if you can draw a family 'tree.' At the end of this lesson you will find a chart called 'Cain and his descendents.'

   ✓ The tree for the sons of Cain is partially filled in for you. By looking at **Genesis 4:17–25,** see if you can fill in the blanks. In one place we also are given information about the wives of one of the sons and about the grandsons.

   ✓ Now that you have filled in the names, go back beside each name and write anything you have learned about this person.

In many schools, museums and TV shows you hear and read stories about early man. You see pictures of humped-over, ape-like creatures living in caves and hitting each other over the head with clubs. These kinds of stories tell you that man was very simple and primitive in those days. They even tell you he couldn't talk intelligently, write or build things. They teach that early man used only stone tools and that many thousands of years passed before metal tools were used. They teach that people learned more and became smarter because they evolved over many generations. But what is really true?

4. Let's review some of the things you could have written about early mankind from Genesis 4.

    ✓ In Genesis 4:17, what did Cain build? _____

    ✓ You read in Genesis 4:20 about Jabal's children.

    Where did they live? _____

    What does the Bible say they had?_____

    Read Genesis 4:21 and find out what Jubal's children did.

    _____

    ✓ Look in Genesis 4:22 and see what a man named Tubal-cain did for a living.

    _____

    _____

So, from today's study you have learned that people in the earliest civilization lived in cities. They also were able to make tents, and some of them lived in these tents with their families, as you live in a house with your family. You also learned that these people raised livestock and made tools of bronze and iron. You saw, too, that they played musical instruments. Because they had musical instruments, you also know that they knew how to build those instruments.

When we look at what some books and schools teach and then we see what God says, we can see that man does not always get his ideas from the Bible. Each of us must decide what we will believe.

5. After Adam sinned, we see Cain sin and murder. Did sin continue to increase? Look at Genesis 4:23 and see what Lamech is boasting to his wives. (Hmmmm—we also see he had two wives.)

_____

_____

So we see that murder did not stop with Cain. Sin was increasing in the world.

The line of Adam through Seth

6. Look now at **Genesis 4:25–26.**

✓ What did God do for Adam and Eve after they lost their son Abel?

_____

✓ What do you see happened after Seth was born? _____

_____

7. Turn now to your observation sheet for Genesis 5. There are a lot of *who's* in this chapter. As you read, instead of putting the names in the margin, we'd like you to put them on yet another family tree chart. At the end of the lesson you will find a family tree titled 'Descendents of Adam.' Using your observation worksheet for Genesis 5, fill in the blanks for Adam's line through Seth. Remember, these are the descendents who began to 'call upon the name of the Lord.' They were still sinners, but they did not leave the presence of the Lord, as Cain's sons and daughters did. From these people would eventually come the seed of the woman, Christ Jesus. That promise is why this is such an important chart.

8. When you finish listing the names in each blank, go back and write beside each name the age of the man when he died. Pretty interesting, isn't it?

9. You have probably noticed a key phrase repeated in this chapter. If you haven't already done so, go back and put a big black box around each mention of the phrase 'and he died.' Why do you suppose God keeps repeating this?

_____

10. Did you notice anything unusual when you read about Enoch in **Genesis 5:21–24?** Write below all that you learned about Enoch.

_____

_____

11. In **Genesis 5:29** we see the first mention of a man named Noah. Write below all you learn about Noah from verses 29–32. We'll study more about Noah in the weeks to come, and this passage will get us started.

_____

How are you doing? Are you 'hanging' with us? Have you seen how even lists of names can tell us some fascinating things about how God has worked with His people?

7 C's Connection: _____

Cain and his descendants

Cain			
E_____			
I_____			
Me_____			
Meth_____			
L_____			
Wife #1 Adah		Wife #2 Z_____	
Ja_____	Ju_____	T_____	Naamah (sister)

Descendants of Adam

Adam	God made him in the likeness of God.	And he died at ☐ years.
S ☐	In Adam's own likeness, according to his image.	And he died at ☐ years.
E ☐		And he died at ☐ years.
K ☐		And he died at ☐ years.
Ma ☐		And he died at ☐ years.
Ja ☐		And he died at ☐ years.
E ☐		And he ☐.
Meth ☐		And he died at ☐ years.
La ☐		And he died at ☐ years.
☐	'This one will give us rest …'	
Shem H ☐ J ☐		

It All Begins With Genesis

Events that led to God's judgment

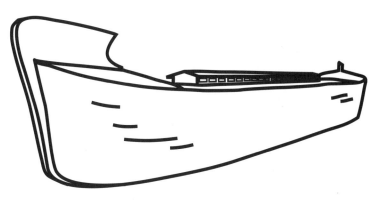

God's Word says, 'The LORD saw that the wickedness of man was great on the earth, and that every intent of the thoughts of his heart was only evil continually' (Genesis 6:5, NAS).

Although Noah warned them about God's coming judgment, the people in Noah's day didn't repent or change their ways. And God brought judgment!

1. Today we begin with some work on your observation sheet for Genesis 6. There are four key words we want you to mark for the whole chapter. They are God, Noah, earth and Ark. After you finish marking the words, we will tell you what to do next. (If time allows, answer the questions you find in the margin of your worksheet.)

    The chapter begins with seven verses that are very hard even for Biblical scholars to understand. They talk about the 'sons of God' and the 'daughters of men,' and they mention the 'Nephilim.' Some people say the 'sons of God' were fallen angels, and others say they were men from the line of Seth, who married the ungodly descendants of Cain. Your teacher will discuss this problem of interpretation in class. Whatever is happening, it has caused the Lord to say, 'Enough!'

2. Do you remember why we mark key words? Is it just to show what pretty colors we can use to decorate our papers? Write below what you are supposed to learn from marking the key words.

    _____

    _____

3. On the chart on the next page, you will find three of the four key words you marked. If a word is a key word, you will learn important truths when it is used. Go back through Genesis 6 again, looking for the times you marked God, Noah and earth. Make a list on the chart of what you can learn from marking each word. (Next week we'll look more closely at what we can learn from the Ark.)

What we learn from key words in Genesis 6

God
(What He thought and did)

Verses 3, 5, 6, 7, 17, 18

Earth
(Condition of man on the earth)

Verses 5, 11, 12, 13, 17

Noah

Verses 8, 9, 10, 13, 18, 22

4. When we look at what was happening in the days of Noah, does it make you think of anything that is happening in our world today? What do you see about our world that is 'corrupt' (that means 'rotten, bad') and violent? How do you think the Lord feels about these things? Might He send another Flood (more about that in Genesis 8)?

_____

_____

5. Noah also appears in the great 'faith' chapter of Hebrews 11.

   Hebrews 11:7 (NIV) 'By faith Noah, when warned about things not yet seen, in holy fear built an ark to save his family. By his faith he condemned the world and became heir of the righteousness that comes by faith.'

   How did Noah become an heir of righteousness?

_____

_____

6. Noah is mentioned again in 2 Peter 2:4–5. Write below what you can learn about Noah from this passage.

   2 Peter 2:4–5 (NIV) 'For if God did not spare angels when they sinned, but sent them to hell, putting them into gloomy dungeons to be held for judgment; if he did not spare the ancient world when he brought the flood on its ungodly people, but protected Noah, a preacher of righteousness, and seven others … .'

_____

_____

_____

_____

7. Noah the righteous was saved. *How?*

    _____

    _____

8. You and I can be saved. *How?*

    _____

    _____

    _____

7 C's Connection: _____

It All Begins With Genesis — LESSON 28

The Flood

Last week we studied God's coming judgment. We learned about the men who warned the people to repent or to turn from their sins and follow the Lord. The people did not turn from their wicked ways, so God sent the Flood to destroy His creation.

For the next four lessons we will be studying the Flood. We will see how God saved Noah, his family and some of the animals from judgment.

There are many people in our society today who make fun of the idea of the Flood. They say it is just a myth, a 'fairy tale,' which couldn't be true. There are also many who believe that there was some sort of Flood, but that it was just a local flood that did not destroy the whole world. This is a very important question to answer. We must see what the Bible really teaches about the event.

1. If you were Noah and God told you to build an Ark, you would have many questions about what to do. Noah lived in a land that wouldn't have much use for a gigantic boat! Fortunately, God was very specific in telling Noah what to do. (Have you noticed that when God tells you something He wants you to do, He always equips you to do it?) Last week you marked 'ark' as one of your key words for Genesis 6. Turn now to verses 14–17 and answer some of the questions Noah needed to have answered by God.

   ✓ God, if I'm going to fill the Ark with animals, how can I keep them from getting all mixed up?

   _____

   _____

   ✓ God, what material should I use to build the Ark?

   _____

   _____

✓ God, how can I make it waterproof?

_____

_____

✓ God, how big should I make the Ark?_____

_____

(Note: this would be at least 450 ft long, 75 ft wide, 45 ft high in our measurements.)

✓ Oh LORD, I expect we need some ventilation, but if I put windows in the Ark, the water will come rushing in. What should I do?

_____

_____

✓ God, should there be more than one floor?

_____

_____

✓ Dear God, what should I do about doors for the Ark?

_____

_____

✓ LORD, what will the animals and people eat? (Read 6:21.)

_____

_____

✓ God, how am I going to be able to get all those animals you want me to put in the Ark? (Read 6:19–20.)

_____

_____

The Ark was large enough to hold 522 modern train cars! Scientists say that a vessel or a ship the size and design of the Ark would be able to float and survive on the raging sea. It would be almost impossible for it to turn over.

2. In the box below, draw a picture of what you think the Ark looked like on the waves.

3. The Old Testament is rich with 'pictures' that foreshadow Christ. The story of Noah and the Ark points to much more than the historical events it records. Think for a few moments and see if you can see some parallels between Noah, the Ark and the Flood and our own salvation from our sins. Write your answer below.

_____

_____

_____

4. The Flood chapters are very important chapters in the Bible. They include chapters 6, 7 and 8. You have already studied chapter 6. Now it is time to take out your observation sheet for chapter 7 and see what else you can learn about the Flood. Answer all the questions found in the margin, if you have time. If you do not have time to complete this assignment, your teacher will help you to identify the key words and phrases that are most important to our study.

5. God was also pretty specific in telling Noah who and what was to go on the Ark. Write below what Noah learned.

✓ Who was to go on the Ark? (Read 7:1–3.)

_____

✓ Who and what was going to be destroyed? (Read 7:20–22.)

_____

In the next lesson we'll imagine what the Flood year would be like, and we'll make a log of the events.

7 C's Connection: _____

It All Begins With Genesis

The voyage of the Ark

In Genesis 7 and 8 we have the story of the actual Flood, and the year spent on the Ark. Isn't it amazing to see how careful Noah was to record the dates and times of that year? It is like a ship's captain might write in his log. Today we're going to make a ship's log of the Flood.

You will need to have your observation sheets for chapters 7 and 8 in front of you as you work. We've started your log for you in order to help you see what to do. As you write the events, think about what it would be like to be someone in Noah's family on the Ark during that time. Be ready to talk about this with your parents or with your class.

The voyage of Noah's Ark

Scripture	Date	What happened
Genesis 7:1–9	Noah was 600 years old. Waited on the Ark for 7 days.	God told us to enter the Ark with all the animals. We obeyed and waited 7 days. God closed the door.
Genesis 7:10–8:4	In the 600th year of Noah's life, in the second month, on the 17th day of the month	All fountains of the great deep burst open …
Genesis 8:4–5a	7th month, 17th day of the month	

Scripture	Date	What happened
Genesis 8:5b	10th month, 1st day of the month	
Genesis 8:6–9	40 days later	
Genesis 8:10–11	7 days later	
Genesis 8:12	7 days later	
Genesis 8:13	In the 601st year, in the first month, on the first day of the month	
Genesis 8:14–22	In the second month, on the 27th day	

1. Ready for a little math? Since you know the day that Noah's family went into the Ark and the day they came out, can you figure out how long they were in the Ark?

2. There are many different ideas about the Flood. Some people think the Flood didn't happen at all. Others think the water covered only the part of the world where Noah lived. This is an important question because it brings up the issue of the truth of the Word of God. Well, let's get back to the source of all truth, God's Word, and see what it says.

    Go to **Genesis 7:19–23.** On your worksheet, circle in red the words 'all' and 'every.' Then answer the questions below.

    ✓ If every high mountain everywhere under the heavens was covered in water, can you think of any way that the Flood was not global?

    _____

    There are other questions you would have to ask if the Flood were just local:

    • **Why did Noah have to build an Ark at all? He could have just migrated to another area.**

    • **Why were the animals collected? They would have migrated.**

    • **How could a local flood destroy the entire earth and its inhabitants?**

    • **Why are there flood legends in almost every people group throughout the world?**

    • **God promised He would never send another flood to destroy the earth. If the Flood was just local, He must have broken His promise, because there are many local floods every year.**

    ✓ Now then, after reading the Scripture above, what would you answer if someone asked you whether the Flood covered the entire earth? Say more than just 'yes' or 'no.' Tell them why. (Note: There are many people who love the Lord who for various reasons believe the Flood was not a worldwide Flood. It doesn't mean they are not Christians. But we all need to study what the Scriptures actually teach. We all need to learn how to think critically and how to lovingly discuss some of the issues of disagreement.)

    _____

    _____

    _____

3. Read Genesis 8:20 and write below the first thing that Noah did after leaving the Ark. Write also why you think Noah did what he did.

_____

_____

_____

4. When the Lord saw what Noah was doing, what did He say to Himself? This is an important promise for us to remember.

_____

_____

_____

7 C's Connection: _____

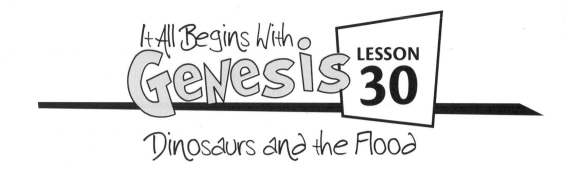

Dinosaurs and the Flood

Did dinosaurs go on and come off the Ark with Noah? Dinosaurs are very interesting and popular these days. However, when you read books about them, you usually hear them used as illustrations for the theory of evolution. You read that they lived and died millions of years before man ever appeared on the earth.

Today we are going to look at dinosaurs and answer some of the most-asked questions—from a biblical worldview.

Are dinosaurs found in the Bible?

The word 'dinosaur' isn't in the Bible because the word itself wasn't invented until 1841, when an Englishman named Richard Owen discovered some bones from a large creature and called it a 'dinosaur,' meaning 'terrible lizard.' Technically, the term refers to land animals only.

There are at least three different words in Scripture that are used to describe large and often fearsome beasts. Let's look at them.

Behemoth

Could Job have been familiar with dinosaurs? Remember, he lived in the years immediately following the Flood, so if dinosaurs came off the Ark, he might have known about them. Read Job 40:15–24 printed below for you. Mark every mention of 'behemoth,' including the pronouns, and note how he is described. (Don't miss verses 17–18.)

(We must be aware of the context of this passage. God is speaking to Job here.)

Job 40:15–24 (NIV) 'Look at the behemoth, which I made along with you and which feeds on grass like an ox. What strength he has in his loins, what power in the muscles of his belly! His tail sways like a cedar; the sinews of his thighs are close-knit. His bones are tubes of bronze, his limbs like rods of iron. He ranks first among the works of God, yet his Maker can approach him with his sword. The hills bring him their produce, and all the wild animals play nearby. Under the lotus plants he lies, hidden among the reeds in the marsh. The lotuses conceal him in their shadow; the poplars by the stream surround him. When the river rages, he is not alarmed; he is secure, though the Jordan should surge against his mouth. Can anyone capture him by the eyes, or trap him and pierce his nose?'

1. What does that description sound like? Possibly something you've seen in museums?

_____

You may find it interesting to note this verse in several different Bible translations. In the margin of many Bibles, you will often see a footnote that describes behemoth as an 'elephant' or a 'hippopotamus.' (Have you ever seen the tail of an elephant and a hippopotamus?) When you see this, it is easy to see that even Bible translators can be influenced by naturalistic presuppositions.

Leviathan

'Leviathan' is another word used for great beasts. It is used six times in Scripture. One example is Psalm 104:26. Highlight what you learn about leviathan from this verse.

> **Psalm 104:24–26** (NIV) 'How many are your works, O LORD! In wisdom you made them all; the earth is full of your creatures. There is the sea, vast and spacious, teeming with creatures beyond number—living things both large and small. There the ships go to and fro, and the leviathan, which you formed to frolic there.'

3. Another description of leviathan is found in Job 41:1–21. Write on the lines that follow what this description reminds you of, and highlight in the text what you read that makes you think so.

> **Job 41:1–21** (NAS) 'Can you draw out Leviathan with a fishhook? Or press down his tongue with a cord? Can you put a rope in his nose or pierce his jaw with a hook? Will he make many supplications to you, or will he speak to you soft words? Will he make a covenant with you? Will you take him for a servant forever? ... Can you fill his skin with harpoons, or his head with fishing spears? Lay your hand on him; remember

the battle; you will not do it again! ... I will not keep silence concerning his limbs or his mighty strength, or his orderly frame. Who can strip off his outer armor? Who can come within his double mail? Who can open the doors of his face? Around his teeth there is terror. ... His sneezes flash forth light, and his eyes are like the eyelids of the morning. Out of his mouth go burning torches; sparks of fire leap forth. Out of his nostrils smoke goes forth as from a boiling pot and burning rushes. His breath kindles coals, and a flame goes forth from his mouth.'

_____

_____

Tannin

This Hebrew word is used 28 times in the Old Testament. It is usually translated 'dragon' (especially in the King James Version.) The verses we've given you below are in the New American Standard version. See if you can tell which word is the Hebrew word *'tannin.'* It isn't always translated with the same English word.

> **Genesis 1:21** 'And God created the great sea monsters, and every living creature that moves, with which the waters swarmed after their kind, and every winged bird after its kind; and God saw that it was good.'

> **Psalm 91:13** 'You will tread upon the lion and cobra, the young lion and the serpent you will trample down.'

> **Psalm 148:7** 'Praise the Lord from the earth, sea monsters and all deeps.'

Did God create dinosaurs? When?

3.   When were dinosaurs created? (Look at Genesis 1:24–25.)

_____

_____

Did dinosaurs go on the Ark?

4. Read **Genesis 6:19–20** and **7:14–15** and answer the question above.

    _____

    _____

    (By the way, most dinosaurs were not any larger than sheep—many no larger than
    a chicken. It is also reasonable to believe that God would not send older, full-grown
    beasts to Noah, but the smaller juveniles. The Ark was big enough.)

5. Were large numbers of dinosaurs buried during the Flood? (See Genesis 7:21.)

    _____

What happened to the dinosaurs after the Flood?

6. We know they came off the Ark. Were conditions in the world different after the
    Flood? Write below what you think dinosaurs might have faced in the immediate
    post-Flood world.

    _____

    _____

7. Did men ever see them? (Remember your Job study.) Do you know of any instances of
    dinosaur-like beasts appearing in literature and art? Have you heard of any modern-
    day sightings of this kind of creature? Could there still be a few of them around? (This
    has to be speculation because the Bible doesn't tell us.) Just share your thoughts on
    this.

    _____

    _____

What is so strange about dinosaurs, anyway? It shouldn't be hard to imagine them living
at the same time as people or giraffes. Some were very large, but most were no larger
than a sheep or a kangaroo. They had big teeth? So do many flesh-eating and plant-eating
creatures alive today! Dinosaurs are merely one group of many animals that have become
extinct, a result you would expect because of the Fall.

Put on the worldview eyeglasses

As we complete our lesson this week, let's go back to what we have been doing this entire year. We have been seeking to see how God views His world, so that we can have a biblical worldview of everything we see about it. We have been contrasting the Biblical worldview with the naturalistic worldview on lots of important questions.

Answer the following, using the appropriate eyeglasses.

8. **Naturalistic worldview.** What does a naturalist see when he looks at dinosaurs through his eyeglasses?

_____

_____

_____

_____

9. **Biblical worldview.** What should someone wearing biblical eyeglasses see when he looks at the subject of dinosaurs?

_____

_____

_____

_____

7 C's Connection: _____

Is there evidence of a worldwide Flood?

Have you ever visited Grand Canyon or other places where the rocks can be clearly seen? We see how beautiful they are, with their many colors and shapes. Many of the rocks are layered one on the other. Some of the layers are lying flat like a layer cake, and others are twisted and buckled.

Do you ever wonder what caused them to be this way?

And what about the fossils? You have seen them in museums and maybe even on mountain hikes. To think they were once living creatures!

Do you ever wonder what caused so many fossils to be buried in the rocks of the earth?

The way people explain the rocks and fossils depends on those eyeglasses we talked about in an earlier lesson—biblical or naturalistic.

We are going to put on the eyeglasses again this week as we look at rocks and fossils.

BIBLICAL WORLDVIEW

Since the Flood described in the book of Genesis was indeed a cataclysmic event, it seems obvious that it would have left some marks on the earth that we could see today. Scientists who believe the biblical account have studied the earth around us and have sought answers to important questions regarding the Flood. We're going to answer three of those questions in today's lesson.

Where did all the water come from?

1. Read **Genesis 7:11–12** once more. Scripture tells us something here about what happened to the earth at the beginning of the Flood.

   'All the _____ of the great _____ burst open, and

   the _____ of the sky were opened. And

   the _____ fell upon the earth for _____ days and _____ nights.'

When we read 'fountains of the great deep,' we understand there was some source of water that came from below the ocean. 'Floodgates of the sky' refers to windows, openings, like sluice gates (gates for controlling irrigation canals). The Bible is using very picturesque language to show that this was a very unusual rainstorm! It might be like we would say, 'It's raining cats and dogs!'

2. It is known that if all the water were wrung out of all the clouds of the entire atmosphere today, the sea level would only be raised about ½ inch! So, rain from the clouds above can't be the only answer.

   Think about this: 70% of the earth's surface is covered with ocean, and the average depth of the oceans is 4,000 meters (more than 13,000 feet). Would that provide enough water to cover the continents? Write in the space below any ideas you have about how the water could have covered the continents.

   _____

   _____

We can't explain exactly what happened, because nobody but God was there to report. Scientists who believe the Bible are studying various ways it might have happened.

When scientists come up with an idea of how something might have happened, they call it a model. Then they look at the data (facts) from all the things they observe, and see how they fit the model.

3. A recent interesting model of how the floodwaters covered the continents has to do with *plate tectonics.* In time we'll have more answers, and clearer models will be proposed. Your teacher will explain this model using the illustrations that follow.

EARTH'S INTERNAL STRUCTURE

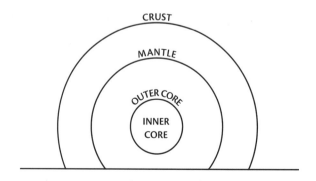

CRUST

MANTLE

OUTER CORE

INNER CORE

Plate tectonics

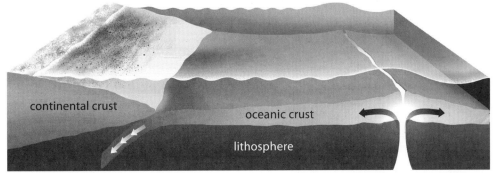

continental crust

oceanic crust

lithosphere

molten rock displaces and pushes the
original ocean crust below the continent

molten rock was releases from inside the
earth and replaces the original ocean crust

4. Now that you have heard the description of the tectonic model, write below your
    understanding of how the waters covered the earth.

_____

_____

What happened during the Flood?

Once the floodwaters began covering the earth,
they would move around a lot of sand, mud,
rocks, trees and once-living creatures. When water
carries material like that in it, it drops the material
('deposits' it), and what we call 'sediment' piles
up. Since the water currents were coming from
different directions, and since different kinds
of sediments were being moved, then different
kinds of piles would result. You might picture
it like a layer cake, with layer after of layer of
sediments being deposited.

Today, all over the world, we see layers of rock
(called 'strata') that have hardened from what
once were water-carried sediments. These kinds of rocks are called 'sedimentary rocks.'

5. Write below your understanding of how the layers in the picture above were formed.

_____

_____

6. Next, consider *fossils.* Fossils are the remains of formerly living plants and animals that have been buried and preserved. Think about the following facts.

    - There are somewhere on the order of ¼ million species of fossil organisms.

    - These are represented by many billions of specimens.

    - They are spread through an average of 1½ miles of sediment over the entire land surface of our planet.

7. As you look through your biblical eyeglasses, how do you think those fossils may have come to be?

_____

Where did all the floodwaters go?

As we continue to look through biblical eyeglasses at the effects of the Flood on the earth, we must answer another difficult question. Where did all the water go after the Flood? What would happen to the land as the floodwaters rushed off?

8. Psalm 104:6–9 may give us a hint. Although it is written in poetic language, it gives us a hint as to what happened to the waters that were 'standing above the mountains.' It is written for you below. Highlight or underline the verse that gives you the hint.

    Psalm 104:6–9 (RSV) 'Thou didst cover it with the deep as with a garment; the waters stood above the mountains. At Thy rebuke they fled; at the sound of thy thunder they took to flight [hurried away]. The mountains rose; the valleys sank down to the place which thou didst appoint [establish] for them. Thou didst set a bound[ary] which they should not pass, so that they might not again cover the earth.'

    When scientists study the record found in the rocks, they observe that a lot of activity must have occurred following the Flood. There was much folding, bending and uplifting of rocks. Many of those sedimentary layers that once looked like a flat cake, now looked like this illustration at the right.

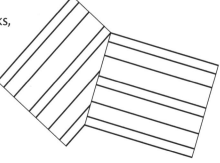

9. Layer upon layer of soft sediments built up as the Flood washed over the land. As the mountains rose up and the waters rushed off them, what do you think might have happened to the land that those waters rushed over?

_____

_____

_____

Once the retreating floodwaters rushed over the land, erosion occurred and canyons formed, and the 'layer cake' pictures given above looked more like the illustration at the right:

After the Flood, we would expect that a long time would be necessary for the earth to 'settle down' from all the activity of the Flood. In fact, some scientists believe that the earthquakes and volcanoes and other geologic activity we experience today are merely leftover effects of the Flood.

They believe that during the first centuries following the Flood, large earthquakes and volcanic eruptions occurred almost daily.

Much of Yellowstone National Park is in a single volcanic cone. This volcano is much larger than any existing volcanoes we know about. It probably erupted during this post-Flood period of time.

It is likely that many of the world's tall mountains (such as the Alps, the Himalayas, the Rockies and even Mount Ararat) rose hundreds to thousands of feet, and that some of the earth's valleys (such as the Dead Sea) dropped during this amazing period of time.

Summary of the Biblical view about how most of the rocks and fossils of the earth formed: FLOOD!

A LOT of water fell in a LITTLE bit of time.

Do you remember what this process is called? _____

NATURALISTIC WORLDVIEW

Not everyone believes the biblical worldview. So, if you don't believe the Bible, how can you explain those rocks, fossils, canyons, etc.? Now it is time to take off your biblical eyeglasses and put on your naturalistic eyeglasses. A naturalistic person looks at the same rocks, fossils and geologic activity, but he comes up with a different model for what caused them.

Until the early nineteenth century, most people believed that most of the rocks and the fossils found on earth were the result of the great Flood of Noah's day. But a lot of people of that day were challenging the Bible and all it said. Miracles were questioned.

A man named Charles Lyell published a textbook of geology in 1830 that said the rocks and fossils could better be explained by the naturalistic view …

Summary of naturalistic view of rocks and fossils:

A LITTLE bit of water and a LOT of TIME.

Do you remember what this is called? _____

A naturalist would say that geologic processes such as sedimentation, erosion and canyon formation are happening very slowly today. They believe that things have always happened that way. Since they have a naturalistic view and don't believe the Bible, there is no reason for them to think that God could have intervened in such a way as the Flood.

10. So, if you have on naturalistic eyeglasses, you must deny a worldwide Flood. You would then look at the layers of sedimentary rock all over the world and would think that they were laid down at the speeds at which we see them being deposited today (perhaps about 1 foot every 5,000–10,000 years). If you are wearing naturalistic eyeglasses, how long would you say it took to form all those layers of sedimentary rock around the world (hundreds, thousands, millions, billions of years)?

    _____

    As you look through those naturalistic eyeglasses, you see the billions of dead things buried in rock layers all over the earth. You believe that life evolved from a single cell, and those fossils in the rock layers were deposited over millions of years. So in this way of thinking, what do these fossils represent?

    _____

Does it all matter? Talk that through with your parent or teacher.

7 C's Connection: _____

After the Flood

oday we are going to step off the Ark with Noah as he begins a life in a new world. We saw in Genesis 8 that Noah began that life by building an altar and worshipping God. Now in Genesis 9 God speaks to Noah.

1. Genesis 9 is full of important information for us. Begin today with your observation sheet for chapter 9 in front of you. Read verses 1–4. God blesses Noah and gives him some important instructions.

   ✓ Some of the instructions sound like what God told Adam in the Garden, don't they? Write below what you see in these verses that remind you of what God told Adam.

   _____

   _____

   ✓ But God changes something here, also. This is different. What will happen in man's relationship to animals? What new permission is given to Noah at this time?

   _____

   _____

   _____

2. Now read **Genesis 9:4–7.** Mark on your worksheet every mention of 'blood.'

   ✓ In our world today, there is much discussion about what is called 'capital punishment' or the death penalty. Even Christians often don't know what to think. Read verse 6 and write out what God's Word has to say about someone who has murdered a person.

   _____

   _____

But what about Exodus 20:13 and the command 'You shall not murder'? Is God contradicting Himself? It is helpful to know that the word 'murder' or 'kill' means to murder or to kill someone on purpose. God knows that sometimes a person is killed by accident, and God does not treat an accident in the same way as a death that happened on purpose. God instituted the practice of capital punishment because He values human life.

✓ Why do you think God is so 'tough' towards those who shed the blood of another? The answer is found in Genesis 9:6. Circle this reason on your observation sheet and write it out below.

_____

_____

3. Now read **Genesis 9:8–17.** This passage includes the first mention in Scripture of a very important word: *covenant*. Mark in a distinctive way every mention of the word 'covenant' in this passage.

Do you know what the word 'covenant' means? A covenant is a promise or agreement that is made between two people or between God and man.

A covenant is a lifelong promise that can never be broken. Sometimes, depending on the terms of the covenant, it goes beyond the lifetime of those who make it. The terms of the covenant are passed on to the children of those who make the covenant.

In our Western culture, the idea of a covenant is difficult to understand. People make and break promises without really thinking much about it at all.

The closest relationship that we can compare is the marriage relationship: a man and woman promise to live together and to love one another until death parts them. Rings are exchanged as a sign of the promise they are making; each time the husband or wife looks at his or her ring, they are reminded of the promises (or vows) they have made and of their relationship to their mate.

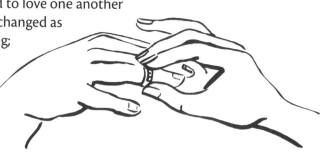

However, in the days in which we live, divorce is very common. Marriages end. People break their promises to one another. But God never breaks His promises to us.

4. Let's see what you learned about the covenant in Genesis 9. Fill in the blanks of the chart below. If you earlier answered the who, what, when, where, why and how kinds of questions as you marked the word 'covenant,' you will already know what to put in the blanks.

Who established the covenant?	
Whom was the covenant with?	
What was the promise of the covenant?	
What was the sign of the covenant?	
How long would the covenant be in effect?	

5. Before we continue with your study of Genesis 9, let's consider for a moment life in this new world. Pretend you are Noah and have just left the Ark. What do you think life would be like after a worldwide Flood? Starting all over again would be a difficult thing. You couldn't go to the local shopping mall or fast-food restaurant for dinner and for the things you need to live!

    Noah's family had only the tools they brought with them on the Ark.

    And think how the earth had been changed by the great Flood. It was probably a pretty scary place. Scientists who wear biblical eyeglasses tell us that following the Flood there were many earthquakes and much volcanic activity going on, much more than in today's world.

6. Scientists who accept the biblical account of the Flood also believe that an Ice Age began in the centuries following the Flood. Does the Bible give us any hints? There may be some in the Book of Job. It is believed Job lived in the centuries following the Flood; it is a very old book. In it we find more references to ice, cold and snow than in any other book of the Bible. Look at each of the verses given to you below and see if you can tell what kind of catastrophe might have been happening. (A catastrophe is a thing that happens suddenly and causes damage and disaster.) Write what you think may have happened in the line under the verse.

✓ **Job 1:16** (NAS) 'While he was still speaking, another came and said, "The fire of God fell from heaven and burned up the sheep and the servants and consumed them, and I alone have escaped to tell you." '

_____

✓ **Job 26:11** (Job is speaking in figurative language, NIV) 'The pillars of the heavens quake, aghast at his rebuke.'

_____

✓ In the following verses, God is speaking to Job in figurative language that Job is familiar with. Underline the references to familiar experiences. (Is this the climate of the Bible lands that we know today?)

Job 38:29–30 (NAS) 'From whose womb has come the ice? And the frost of heaven, who has given it birth? Water becomes hard like stone, and the surface of the deep is imprisoned.'

7. It is interesting to think about how the Flood may have led to the Ice Age.

After the Flood, the oceans were still very warm, and that caused the air over the oceans to be warm and wet (humid).

But the air over the continents (the land) was cool and dry.

This resulted in great air movements and a lot of rainfall.

These conditions may have lasted 500–1,000 years.

All along the world's oceans there was a humid tropical climate (because of the warm water), but it was cool and dry over the continents. This forced air (and precipitation) over the continents. Many areas now dry were wet then (for example, the Dead Sea, Death Valley).

Towards the end of this period the precipitation fell as snow in the high latitudes and high altitudes, and ice accumulated. Eventually the ice surged (moved forward) under its own weight, rapidly advancing over the land.

The mountains of ice and snow that advanced across the land are known as glaciers. We have glaciers in some high latitudes today, but at the time following the Flood, there were many glaciers in the high latitudes and high altitudes of the world.

The ice may have advanced and then melted in only a few decades. (A decade is 10 years.)

8. In the space provided below, draw a picture of what you think the world looked like to Noah and his family.

9. Let's return now to your observation sheets for Genesis 9. Read verses 18 and 19. Circle the people who came off the Ark. What do we learn from this passage about these three sons of Noah? Circle the verse that answers this important question, and write it below.

_____

_____

10. Read **Genesis 9:20–27.** This tells of an event that happened in Noah's life after he began farming. Circle on your observation sheet every person mentioned in this account. Answer the Five W's and H questions below.

   ✓ *What* happened to Noah? _____

   ✓ *How* did Noah's son Ham react to his father?

   _____

   ✓ *What* was Shem's and Japheth's reaction to their father's nakedness?

   _____

   _____

   ✓ Later, Noah gave a curse and blessing and some prophecy. This will become very interesting as we later trace the genealogies of Shem, Ham and Japheth. Write below what Noah had to say about Canaan. (Do you wonder why Noah cursed Canaan, the son of Ham, instead of Ham directly? A lot of theologians wonder that, too!)

   _____

   _____

   _____

   ✓ What did Noah say about Shem?

   _____

   _____

   _____

   ✓ What did Noah say about Japheth?

   _____

   _____

11. Read verses 28–29.

    ✓ Is the Curse from the Fall of mankind still in effect? How do we know?

    _____

    ✓ How long did Noah live after the Flood? _____

    ✓ At what age did Noah die? _____

12. When we talk about the Flood and the years following the Flood, what kind of eyeglasses are we wearing, biblical or naturalistic?

13. What would a person who didn't believe in God say about the Flood of Noah and about the Ice Age that followed?

    _____

    _____

    _____

7 C's Connection: _____

Different languages, peoples, nations?

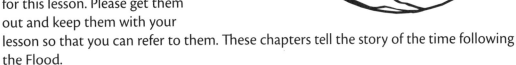

When Noah left the Ark, there were only eight human beings left in the whole world. They were all members of the same family who probably looked pretty much alike. They spoke the same language. Now we have many different peoples scattered all over the earth, with different colored skin and features, speaking many different languages. What happened?

You will need your observation worksheets for Genesis 10 and 11 for this lesson. Please get them out and keep them with your lesson so that you can refer to them. These chapters tell the story of the time following the Flood.

1. Genesis 10 and 11 seem sort of confusing. In chapter 10, we learn about the descendents of Shem, Ham and Japheth and how they spread out and how different languages, families and nations were formed. Then in chapter 11, we have a 'flash back,' where we are told how it happened that different languages, families and nations were formed. Check it out for a moment.

   Read quickly through chapters 10 and 11. There are only a few things you are asked to mark on your observation sheet. For now we just want you to see how one chapter fits with another and what is talked about.

   ✓ Now look at your observation worksheet for chapter 10. How does verse 1 begin? (Have you seen that phrase anywhere else in Genesis?)

   _____

✓ Go next to chapter 11 to see what story is reported in the first eight verses. Write it below.

_____

✓ Which happened first, the events of chapter 10 or the event of chapter 11?

_____

Interesting, yes? This week we'll study the event in chapter 11 and then in our last lesson we'll go to chapter 10 and look at what happened once those events were completed.

2. When Noah and his family left the Ark, God gave him a command. Read Genesis 9:1 and write below what God wanted Noah to do.

_____

3. It seems like Noah and his family obeyed the first part of the command because these chapters are full of lists of his descendants. But what about the second part of the command 'to fill the earth'? Read Genesis 11:2. They journeyed for a while, but what did they do when they arrived in the land of Shinar?

_____

4. God wanted them to fill the whole earth, but instead they settled in one place. Perhaps the post-Flood world was so inhospitable that they wanted to stay close on the plain where it would be safe. But what happened when they settled there on that plain? Fill in the blanks about what happened in verses 3–4.

'Come let us make bricks and burn them thoroughly. Come, let us build

_____ a city, and a tower whose top will

reach into heaven, and let us make _____
a name; lest we be scattered abroad over the face of the whole earth.'

5. Was there anything wrong with building a city? Look at the pronouns used in verses 3–4. Circle them in red. Do they give you a clue? Write your answer below.

_____

_____

_____

_____

6. Why was the Lord concerned about what they were doing? Why was it wrong?

_____

_____

_____

_____

_____

7. 'Wie wordest du fuhlen: Du stehst mit deinen Freunden in einer Gruppe. Plotzlich fangt jeder an in einer anderen Sprache zu sprechen. Einer spricht Deutsch, einer spricht Franzosisch, einer spricht Chinesish und einer English. Heute, studierst du den anfang der Sprachen.'

Do you know what that paragraph says? If you don't, that means you don't read German! Here is what it means in English:

'How would you feel if you were standing with a group of your friends and each of them began to speak a different language? One spoke German; one spoke French; one spoke Chinese; you spoke English. Today you are studying the beginning of languages.'

What would you do in that kind of situation?

_____

_____

8. Most of us would feel uncomfortable because we couldn't understand what others were saying and we couldn't make ourselves understood. We would find someone who spoke our language and would stay with them. Read Genesis 11:7–9. Write below what the Lord did and what happened after that.

_____

_____

_____

9. Now we have learned why people spread out over the face of the earth. **Genesis 10:31–32** tells us how the people on the earth were divided. Read the verse in your observation worksheet and fill in the blanks below:

'These are the sons of Shem, according to their _____, according to

their _____, by their _____,

according to their _____; these are the families of the sons of

Noah, according to their _____, by their _____; and

out of these the nations _____ on the earth after the Flood.'

10. Do you ever wonder how what we call 'races' formed? How did Noah's family result in people with black, yellow and white skins, plus all the other features we consider racial? How many 'races' do we have in the world today?

How do 'races' form? Could they all come from one family?

There is an exercise you can do that will help illustrate some genetics. It will explain how the different nationalities could form.

11. As we put the pieces together about what happened there on the plain of Shinar, we need to look at one more passage. It is found in Genesis 10:8–11. Read through those verses in your observation worksheet and mark the name 'Nimrod' and every pronoun that refers to him. Then answer the following Five W's and H questions:

✓ *Who* was the father of Nimrod? _____

✓ *Who* was the grandfather of Nimrod? (In other words, was he a grandson of Shem, Ham or Japheth?)

_____

✓ *How* is Nimrod described in these verses?

_____

_____

✓ *What* was Nimrod's first kingdom called?

_____

✓ It seems like Nimrod had many kingdoms. Do you know your Biblical history? Did the kingdom of Babel go on to become a good kingdom or a wicked one?

_____

✓ Verse 11 tells us that he went somewhere else, a city and country that became very famous because it was the country that was to conquer the Northern Kingdom of Israel and take them into captivity. What was the name of that evil city and country?

_____

✓ So, when the Scripture refers to Nimrod as being a 'mighty hunter before the Lord,' do you think he played a good role or a bad role in the events at the Tower of Babel?

_____

_____

12. If time permits, circle the theme and draw pictures to represent the themes of chapters 10 and 11.

7 C's Connection: _____

God's plan for His world unfolds

As we have studied Genesis for many, many weeks, we have been trying to help you put on the kind of eyeglasses that let you see the world the way God sees it. That will give you a biblical worldview that will help you to understand life as you experience it.

In this our last lesson we want to see how God's plan in Genesis is beginning to unfold and go out to the whole world.

And, believe it or not, we see this by making more 'family trees'!

1. You have studied why the people spread out over the face of the earth. **Genesis 10:31–32** tells us how the people on the earth were divided. As you review, what do you learn?

    'These are the sons of Shem, according to their _____, according to

    their _____, by their _____, according

    to their _____; these are the families of the sons of Noah,

    according to their _____, by their _____; and

    out of these the nations _____ on the earth after the Flood.'

2. You will need to have your worksheets for Genesis 9–11 beside you. Look first at chapter 10. Family trees (called 'genealogies') are very important in Scripture. Yes, there are a lot of big words we can't spell or say, and most of the names we haven't even heard. But God wanted us to have a record of His story throughout time, and by following the story of God's people, we will finally come to Jesus. History is really His story. Let's have some fun seeing what we can learn from all these names.

3. Just for review, write below the names of Noah's three sons, because it is from them that all the people of the earth would come.

    _____

4. In chapter 10 we find 'family trees' for each of Noah's sons. Before we draw those trees, look at Genesis 11:10 to see another family tree.

    Whose descendents are talked about in chapter 11? _____

    Hmmm ... that's strange. Shem's sons are listed in chapter 10 and again in chapter 11. Was Moses confused? (Are *you* confused?) No, he wasn't confused. There is a good reason why Shem's descendents are described in more detail than the descendents of Ham and Japheth. Stay tuned ... we'll figure it out.

5. The first family tree we will draw is of the sons of Japheth. Read Genesis 10:2–4 and fill in the blanks on the 'tree' below.

    Japheth had seven sons:

    _____

    _____

    Japheth's son *Gomer* had three sons:

    A_____ R_____ To_____

    Japheth's son *Javan* had four sons:

    E_____ T_____

    K_____ D_____

6. Japheth's genealogy doesn't give us a lot of detail, does it? We don't really know why. Perhaps these families spread out so far that the information about all their children did not get back to the writer of Genesis in order for him to record all of the family information. In any case, the purpose of this passage is to show what families were around at the time of the Tower of Babel and how the languages were divided at that time. God's purpose was not to give us a detailed genealogy.

Where did the family of Japheth go? At the end of this lesson you will find a map of the world that shows where we think some of these families settled. This map is taken from the International Inductive Study Bible. Look at the names of Japheth's family above, and if you see their names on the map, color them *blue*. Color the arrow for Japheth blue as well.

When you see where the colors are mostly blue, write below what parts of the world were settled by the sons of Japheth.

_____

_____

7. Now it is time to draw the family tree for the sons of Ham. Do you have your observation worksheet for Genesis 10 in front of you? Look at verses 6–14. Fill in the blank places on the chart.

    Ham had four sons:

    _____

    Ham's son *Cush* had six sons:

    _____

    _____

    (Sabteca had two sons: Sheba and Dedan)

    Cush's most famous son (verse 8): N_____

    (He is a very important son. You studied him in your previous lesson.)

    Ham's son Canaan was the Father of the Canaanite Peoples. Some of the Canaanites were

    _____

    _____

8. How did you do with all those big words? Could you pronounce them? ☺ They are important in history because the Canaanites lived in the lands promised to Israel. They became enemies of the Israelites. They included many people who did wicked things, such as worshipping idols and sacrificing their children. God judged those wicked people by allowing the children of Israel to come in and conquer the land where they lived.

   Look at **Genesis 10:19** and look at the places where the Canaanites lived. Do you recognize any of the names of places listed? One place became very famous, and you will study it later in Genesis 19. It is the place where Abraham's nephew Lot would someday live. If you know it, write it below.

   _____

9. Where did the family of Ham go? At the end of this lesson you will find a map of the world that shows where we think some of these families settled. Look at the names of Ham's family above, and if you see their names on the map, color them *green*. Color the arrow for Ham green as well.

   When you see where the colors are mostly green, write below what parts of the world were settled by the sons of Ham.

   _____

   _____

10. In Genesis 9, God gave Noah a prophecy concerning his sons. Although we are now in chapter 11, we need to go back and look at what Noah said. It will help us to remember and understand more about the families of Noah.

   Take out your observation worksheet for chapter 9 and read verses 25–27. This happens after Noah had become drunk from the wine he had made, and he was upset at what his youngest son Ham had done. He speaks first to Ham. What he says is rather strange, because he talks about Ham's son, not Ham directly.

Write below what Noah says about Canaan, a son of Ham, in verses 25 and 26.

_____

_____

11. Now see what God says about Noah's son Japheth. Read verse 27 and write it below.

_____

12. Now what do you learn about Noah's son Shem? He is mentioned in verses 26 and 27. What does Noah say about Shem?

_____

_____

13. So we see that the Lord is the God of Shem. And that Japheth will dwell in the tents of Shem, and Canaan will be his servant. Shem seems to have a special place in God's plan, doesn't he? Let's look next at his family 'tree.' (This is a little trickier, because it is found in *both* chapter 10 and chapter 11 of Genesis.)

We begin by seeing in Genesis 10:22 that Shem had five sons. Fill in the blanks below as we see their names.

Shem had five sons:

_____ .

One of Shem's sons, *Arpachshad*, was especially important to God. We see this because in Genesis 11 the Bible gives great detail about Arpachshad's sons. Turn now to chapter 11, beginning with verse 10. Fill in the blanks where you see things left out.

Noah

Shem

Arpachshad

_____ (Genesis 10:13)

_____ (Genesis 10:14)

Eber

_____ (Genesis 10:16)

Reu

Serug

Nahor

_____ (Genesis 10:27)

_____ (look at Matthew 1:2)

J_____

Judah

Jesse

_____ (look at Matthew 1:6)

Joseph, the husband of Mary

_____ (look at Matthew 1:16)

14 Now that you have completed Shem's family tree, why do you think God gave more information about Shem's family than about Noah's other two sons?

_____

15 Where did the family of Shem go? Look at the world map on the next page and find the names of Shem's family above. Wherever you see their names on the map, color them *yellow.* Color the arrow for Shem yellow as well.

When you see where the colors are mostly yellow, write below what parts of the world were settled by the sons of Shem.

_____

_____

7 C's Connection: _____

Well, you've done it!

You have studied the first eleven chapters of Genesis and have a solid foundation for understanding the whole Bible. You have seen how God created a wonderful world. You learned about the Fall and how the world was changed because of man's sin. And you have seen how God planned even from the beginning to save man by sending a Redeemer.

Now you are able to see God's world through His eyeglasses. You are on your way to having a biblical worldview.

'From these the nations were separated into their lands, every one according to his language, according to their families into their nations' (Genesis 10:5).

It All Begins With Genesis 1

Observation Sheet: Genesis 1

There is a WHO mentioned in verse 1. Make a purple crown around the word every time this 'who' is mentioned in the chapter (because He is King of the universe).

1 In the beginning God created the heavens and the earth.

2 And the earth was formless and void, and darkness was over the surface of the deep; and the Spirit of God was moving over the surface of the waters.

3 Then God said, 'Let there be light'; and there was light.

4 And God saw that the light was good; and God separated the light from the darkness.

Write below WHAT was created on Day 1.

5 And God called the light day, and the darkness He called night. And there was evening and there was morning, one day.

6 Then God said, 'Let there be an expanse in the midst of the waters, and let it separate the waters from the waters.'

7 And God made the expanse, and separated the waters which were below the expanse from the waters which were above the expanse; and it was so.

Write below WHAT was created on Day 2.

8 And God called the expanse heaven. And there was evening and there was morning, a second day.

9   Then God said, 'Let the waters below the heavens be

gathered into one place, and let the dry land appear'; and

it was so.

10   And God called the dry land earth, and the gathering of

the waters He called seas; and God saw that it was good.

WHAT was created on
Day 3?

11   Then God said, 'Let the earth sprout vegetation, plants

yielding seed, and fruit trees bearing fruit after their kind;

with seed in them, on the earth'; and it was so.

12   And the earth brought forth vegetation, plants yielding

seed after their kind, and trees bearing fruit, with seed in

them, after their kind; and God saw that it was good.

13   And there was evening and there was morning, a third day.

14   Then God said, 'Let there be lights in the expanse of the

heavens to separate the day from the night, and let them

be for signs, and for seasons, and for days and years;

15   and let them be for lights in the expanse of the heavens to

give light on the earth'; and it was so.

WHAT was created on
Day 4?

16   And God made the two great lights; the greater light to

govern the day, and the lesser light to govern the night; He

made the stars also.

17 And God placed them in the expanse of the heavens to

give light on the earth,

18 and to govern the day and the night, and to separate the

light from the darkness; and God saw that it was good.

19 And there was evening and there was morning, a fourth

day.

20 Then God said, 'Let the waters teem with swarms of living

creatures and let birds fly above the earth in the open

expanse of the heavens.'

WHAT was created on
Day 5?

21 And God created the great sea monsters, and every living

creature that moves, with which the waters swarmed after

their kind, and every winged bird after its kind; and God

saw that it was good.

22 And God blessed them, saying, 'Be fruitful and multiply,

and fill the waters in the seas, and let birds multiply on the

earth.'

23 And there was evening and there was morning, a fifth day.

WHAT was created on
Day 6?

24 Then God said, 'Let the earth bring forth living creatures

after their kind: cattle and creeping things and beasts of

the earth after their kind'; and it was so.

25 And God made the beasts of the earth after their kind,

and the cattle after their kind, and everything that creeps

on the ground after its kind; and God saw that it was

good.

There is another WHO mentioned here. Use a stick figure to mark every mention of this WHO in the chapter. This includes the pronouns that mean the same thing.

26 Then God said, 'Let Us make man in Our image, according

to Our likeness; and let them rule over the fish of the sea

and over the birds of the sky and over the cattle and over

all the earth, and over every creeping thing that creeps on

the earth.'

27 And God created man in His own image, in the image of

God He created him; male and female He created them.

28 And God blessed them; and God said to them, 'Be fruitful

and multiply, and fill the earth, and subdue it; and rule

over the fish of the sea and over the birds of the sky, and

over every living thing that moves on the earth.'

29 Then God said, 'Behold, I have given you every plant

yielding seed that is on the surface of all the earth, and

every tree which has fruit yielding seed; it shall be food for

you;

30 and to every beast of the earth and to every bird of the sky

and to every thing that moves on the earth which has life,

I have given every green plant for food'; and it was so.

31 And God saw all that He had made, and behold, it was

very good. And there was evening and there was morning,

the sixth day.

Note: The observation sheets use the New American Standard
version.

Theme of Genesis 1

Circle the best theme (a theme is the subject that is most talked about in the chapter).

    A. God creates everything in the world and universe.

    B. God makes the sea monsters.

    C. God says everything is good.

Draw below a picture of the theme you chose for Genesis 1.

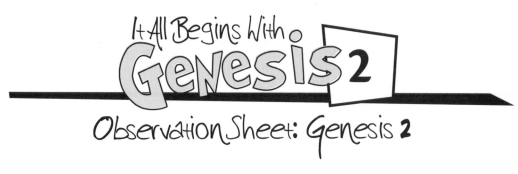
Observation Sheet: Genesis 2

Mark WHO (God) every time He is mentioned in chapter 2. Mark Him the same way you did in chapter 1.

1 Thus the heavens and the earth were completed, and all their hosts.

2 And by the seventh day God completed His work which He had done; and He rested on the seventh day from all His work which He had done.

WHAT did God do on Day 7?

3 Then God blessed the seventh day and sanctified it, because in it He rested from all His work which God had created and made.

4 This is the account of the heavens and the earth when they were created, in the day that the LORD God made earth and heaven.

You have another WHO here. Mark him like you did in chapter 1.

5 Now no shrub of the field was yet in the earth, and no plant of the field had yet sprouted, for the LORD God had not sent rain upon the earth; and there was no man to cultivate the ground.

6 But a mist used to rise from the earth and water the whole surface of the ground.

WHAT events are described in verses 7 and 8?

7   Then the Lord God formed man of dust from the ground, and breathed into his nostrils the breath of life; and man became a living being.

There is a WHERE answered here. Highlight or color it green.

8   And the Lord God planted a garden toward the east, in Eden; and there He placed the man whom He had formed.

9   And out of the ground the Lord God caused to grow every tree that is pleasing to the sight and good for food; the tree of life also in the midst of the garden and the tree of the knowledge of good and evil.

10 Now a river flowed out of Eden to water the garden; and from there it divided and became four rivers.

There are some WHERE's here. Color the place names green.

11 The name of the first is Pishon; it flows around the whole land of Havilah, where there is gold.

12 And the gold of that land is good; the bdellium and the onyx stone are there.

13 And the name of the second river is Gihon; it flows around the whole land of Cush.

14 And the name of the third river is Tigris; it flows east of Assyria. And the fourth river is the Euphrates.

15   Then the LORD God took the man and put him into the

garden of Eden to cultivate it and keep it.

Write below WHAT
the warning is that
God gave to the man.

16   And the LORD God commanded the man, saying, 'From

any tree of the garden you may eat freely;

17   but from the tree of the knowledge of good and evil you

shall not eat, for in the day that you eat from it you shall

surely die.'

18   Then the LORD God said, 'It is not good for the man to be

alone; I will make him a helper suitable for him.'

Write below the event
that takes place in
verses 19–20.

19   And out of the ground the LORD God formed every beast of

the field and every bird of the sky, and brought them to the

man to see what he would call them; and whatever the man

called a living creature, that was its name.

20   And the man gave names to all the cattle, and to the birds

of the sky, and to every beast of the field, but for Adam

there was not found a helper suitable for him.

Write below the event
that takes place in
verses 21–22.

21   So the LORD God caused a deep sleep to fall upon the man,

and he slept; then He took one of his ribs, and closed up

the flesh at that place.

There is a new WHO here. Use a pink stick figure throughout the chapter.

22 And the LORD God fashioned into a woman the rib which He had taken from the man, and brought her to the man.

23 And the man said, 'This is now bone of my bones and flesh of my flesh; she shall be called Woman, because she was taken out of Man.'

This is the beginning (origin) of something. What does God begin here?

24 For this cause a man shall leave his father and his mother, and shall cleave to his wife; and they shall become one flesh.

25 And the man and his wife were both naked and were not ashamed.

Theme of Genesis 2

Circle the best theme (what is talked about the most). Then draw a picture that illustrates it.

A. Adam names the animals.

B. God creates man and woman and gives them a Garden.

C. God makes the Garden of Eden.

Observation Sheet: Genesis 3

Mark all the *who's* you see in the chapter—woman, man, God—as you have already been marking them.
Verse 1 introduces a new WHO. We suggest you mark him with a red pitchfork.

1 Now the serpent was more crafty than any beast of the field which the LORD God had made. And he said to the woman, 'Indeed, has God said, "You shall not eat from any tree of the garden?" '

2 And the woman said to the serpent, 'From the fruit of the trees of the garden we may eat;

3 but from the fruit of the tree which is in the middle of the garden, God has said, "You shall not eat from it or touch it lest you die." '

4 And the serpent said to the woman, 'You surely shall not die!

5 For God knows that in the day you eat from it your eyes will be opened, and you will be like God, knowing good and evil.'

There is a 'first' found in these verses. Write below what it is.

6 When the woman saw that the tree was good for food, and that it was a delight to the eyes, and that the tree was desirable to make one wise, she took from its fruit and ate; and she gave also to her husband with her, and he ate.

3

WHERE do these events occur? Circle or highlight places in green.

WHAT did Adam and Eve do after they sinned?

7   Then the eyes of both of them were opened, and they knew that they were naked; and they sewed fig leaves together and made themselves loin coverings.

8   And they heard the sound of the LORD God walking in the garden in the cool of the day, and the man and his wife hid themselves from the presence of the LORD God among the trees of the garden.

9   Then the LORD God called to the man, and said to him, 'Where are you?'

10 And he said, 'I heard the sound of You in the garden, and I was afraid because I was naked; so I hid myself.'

11 And He said, 'Who told you that you were naked? Have you eaten from the tree of which I commanded you not to eat?'

Who is cursed? What is the curse?

12 And the man said, 'The woman whom Thou gavest to be with me, she gave me from the tree, and I ate.'

13 Then the LORD God said to the woman, 'What is this you have done?' And the woman said, 'The serpent deceived me, and I ate.'

What is the woman's punishment?

14 And the L ORD God said to the serpent, 'Because you have done this, cursed are you more than all cattle and more than every beast of the field; on your belly shall you go, and dust shall you eat all the days of your life;

15 and I will put enmity between you and the woman, and between your seed and her seed; he shall bruise you on the head, and you shall bruise him on the heel.'

What is the man's punishment?

16 To the woman He said, 'I will greatly multiply your pain in childbirth; in pain you shall bring forth children; yet your desire shall be for your husband, and he shall rule over you.'

17 Then to Adam He said, 'Because you have listened to the voice of your wife, and have eaten from the tree about which I commanded you, saying, "You shall not eat from it"; 'cursed is the ground because of you; in toil you shall eat of it all the days of your life.

18 Both thorns and thistles it shall grow for you; and you shall eat the plants of the field;

What did the L ORD God do for Adam and Eve?

19 by the sweat of your face you shall eat bread, till you return to the ground, because from it you were taken; for you are dust, and to dust you shall return.'

20 Now the man called his wife's name Eve, because she was the mother of all the living.

21 And the LORD God made garments of skin for Adam and his wife, and clothed them.

There are some WHERE's here. Color or circle in Green.

22 Then the LORD God said, 'Behold, the man has become like one of us, knowing good and evil and now, lest he stretch out his hand, and take also from the tree of life, and eat, and live forever'—

23 therefore the LORD God sent him out from the garden of Eden, to cultivate the ground from which he was taken.

24 So He drove the man out; and at the east of the garden of Eden He stationed the cherubim, and the flaming sword which turned every direction, to guard the way to the tree of life.

Theme of Genesis 3

Circle the best theme and then draw a picture below to illustrate that theme.

A. The serpent

B. The sin of Adam and Eve

C. Adam and Eve sent from the Garden

It All Begins With Genesis 4

Observation Sheet: Genesis 4

You have some new *who*'s to mark in this chapter. You already know how to mark God, Adam and Eve, but now you need to come up with ways to mark Cain and Abel. There are many other names at the end of the chapter, but you don't need to mark them at this time.

There is a 'first' event in verse 1. What is it?

Verse 3 gives us another 'first' event. Write it below.

1 Now the man had relations with his wife Eve, and she conceived and gave birth to Cain, and she said, 'I have gotten a manchild with the help of the LORD.'

2 And again, she gave birth to his brother Abel. And Abel was a keeper of flocks, but Cain was a tiller of the ground.

3 So it came about in the course of time that Cain brought an offering to the LORD of the fruit of the ground.

4 And Abel, on his part also brought of the firstlings of his flock and of their fat portions. And the LORD had regard for Abel and for his offering;

5 but for Cain and his offering He had no regard. So Cain became very angry and his countenance fell.

6 Then The LORD said to Cain, 'Why are you angry? And why has your countenance fallen?

7 If you do well, will not your countenance be lifted up? And if you do not do well, sin is crouching at the door and its desire is for you, but you must master it.'

Another 'first' event is listed in verse 8. Write it below.

8 And Cain told Abel his brother. And it came about when they were in the field, that Cain rose up against Abel his brother and killed him.

9 Then the LORD said to Cain, 'Where is Abel your brother?' And he said, 'I do not know. Am I my brother's keeper?'

10 And He said, 'What have you done? The voice of your brother's blood is crying to Me from the ground.

What 'curse' did God give to Cain?

11 And now you are cursed from the ground which has opened its mouth to receive your brother's blood from your hand.

12 When you cultivate the ground it shall no longer yield its strength to you; you shall be a vagrant and a wanderer on the earth.'

13 And Cain said to the LORD, 'My punishment is too great to bear!

14 Behold, Thou hast driven me this day from the face of the ground; and from Thy face I shall be hidden, and   I shall be a vagrant and a wanderer on the earth, and it will come about that whoever finds me will kill me.'

15 So the LORD said to him, 'Therefore whoever kills Cain, vengeance will be taken on him sevenfold.' And the LORD appointed a sign for Cain, lest anyone finding him should slay him.

There is a WHERE in verse 16. Highlight or circle it in green.

16 Then Cain went out from the presence of the LORD, and settled in the land of Nod, east of Eden.

There is another 'first' event in verse 17. Write it below.

17 And Cain had relations with his wife and she conceived, and gave birth to Enoch; and he built a city and called the name of the city Enoch, after the name of his son.

18 Now to Enoch was born Irad; and Irad became the father of Mehujael; and Mehujael became the father of Methushael; and Methushael became the father of Lamech.

19 And Lamech took to himself two wives: the name of the one was Adah; and the name of the other, Zillah.

See if you can tell what 'first' is mentioned in verse 20.

20 And Adah gave birth to Jabal; he was the father of those who dwell in tents and have livestock.

Another 'first' is mentioned in verse 21.

21 And his brother's name was Jubal; he was the father of all those who play the lyre and pipe.

22   As for Zillah, she also gave birth to Tubal-cain, the forger of

all implements of bronze and iron; and the sister of Tubal-

cain was Naamah.

23   And Lamech said to his wives, 'Adah and Zillah, listen to

my voice. You wives of Lamech give heed to my speech,

for I have killed a man for wounding me; and a boy for

striking me.

How can you see the
results of the Fall in
verses 24–25?

24   'If Cain is avenged sevenfold, then Lamech seventy-

sevenfold.'

25   And Adam had relations with his wife again: and she gave

birth to a son, and named him Seth, for, she said, 'God has

appointed me another offspring in place of Abel; for Cain

killed him.'

What happened after
Seth was born?

26   And to Seth, to him also a son was born; and he called his

name Enosh. Then men began to call upon the name of

the LORD.

Theme of Genesis 4

Circle the best theme:

    A. Cain and Abel

    B. Cain finds a wife and builds a city.

    C. The offerings of Cain and Abel

Draw below a picture of the theme you chose for Genesis 4.

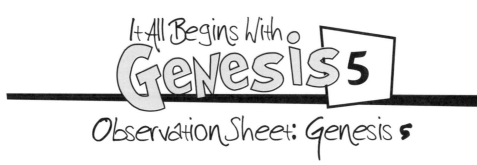

Observation Sheet: Genesis 5

Verse 1 gives us once again the repeated phrase we see in Genesis. Make a big box around this verse.

There are *lots* of *who's* in this chapter. Circle each different person named.

There are also lots of time indicators—how long each person lived. Underline these or make a clock by each.

A very important key phrase appears for the first time in
verse 5. Make a big black box around it every time it appears in this chapter.

1   This is the book of the generations of Adam. In the day when God created man, He made him in the likeness of God.

2   He created them male and female, and He blessed them and named them Man in the day when they were created.

3   When Adam had lived one hundred and thirty years, he became the father of a son in his own likeness, according to his image, and named him Seth.

4   Then the days of Adam after he became the father of Seth were eight hundred years, and he had other sons and daughters.

5   So all the days that Adam lived were nine hundred and thirty years, and he died.

6   And Seth lived one hundred and five years, and became the father of Enosh.

7   Then Seth lived eight hundred and seven years after he became the father of Enosh, and he had other sons and daughters.

8   So all the days of Seth were nine hundred and twelve years, and he died.

9   And Enosh lived ninety years, and became the father of Kenan.

10 Then Enosh lived eight hundred and fifteen years after he became the father of Kenan, and he had other sons and daughters.

11 So all the days of Enosh were nine hundred and five years, and he died.

12 And Kenan lived seventy years, and became the father of Mahalalel.

13 Then Kenan lived eight hundred and forty years after he became the father of Mahalalel, and he had other sons and daughters.

14 So all the days of Kenan were nine hundred and ten years, and he died.

15 And Mahalalel lived sixty-five years, and became the father of Jared.

16 Then Mahalalel lived eight hundred and thirty years after
he became the father of Jared, and he had other sons and
daughters.

17 So all the days of Mahalalel were eight hundred and
ninety-five years, and he died.

18 And Jared lived one hundred and sixty-two years, and
became the father of Enoch.

19 Then Jared lived eight hundred years after he became the
father of Enoch, and he had other sons and daughters.

20 So all the days of Jared were nine hundred and sixty-two
years, and he died.

21 And Enoch lived sixty-five years, and became the father of
Methuselah.

22 Then Enoch walked with God three hundred years after he
became the father of Methuselah, and he had other sons
and daughters.

23 So all the days of Enoch were three hundred and sixty-five
years.

24 And Enoch walked with God; and he was not, for God took him.

25 And Methuselah lived one hundred and eighty-seven years, and became the father of Lamech.

26 Then Methuselah lived seven hundred and eighty-two years after he became the father of Lamech, and he had other sons and daughters.

27 So all the days of Methuselah were nine hundred and sixty-nine years, and he died.

28 And Lamech lived one hundred and eighty-two years, and became the father of a son.

29 Now he called his name Noah, saying, 'This one shall give us rest from our work and from the toil of our hands arising from the ground which the LORD has cursed.'

30 Then Lamech lived five hundred and ninety-five years after he became the father of Noah, and he had other sons and daughters.

31 So all the days of Lamech were seven hundred and seventy-seven years, and he died.

32 And Noah was five hundred years old, and Noah became

the father of Shem, Ham, and Japheth.

Theme of Genesis 5

Circle the best theme:

    A. Adam's sons

    B. Adam lives 930 years.

    C. Enoch and Noah

Draw below a picture of the theme you chose for Genesis 5. (We can't wait to see how you draw this one!)

Observation Sheet: Genesis 6

There are many *who*'s in this chapter. However, the main ones to mark in a distinctive way throughout the chapter are God and Noah.

1 Now it came about, when men began to multiply on the face of the land, and daughters were born to them,

2 that the sons of God saw that the daughters of men were beautiful; and they took wives for themselves, whomever they chose.

There is a time reference in verse 3, a WHEN. Mark time references by drawing a little clock by the verse.

3 Then the LORD said, 'My Spirit shall not strive with man forever, because he also is flesh; nevertheless his days shall be one hundred and twenty years.'

4 The Nephilim were on the earth in those days, and also afterward, when the sons of God came in to the daughters of men, and they bore children to them. Those were the mighty men who were of old, men of renown.

5 Then the LORD saw that the wickedness of man was great on the earth, and that every intent of the thoughts of his heart was only evil continually.

6 And the LORD was sorry that He had made man on the earth, and He was grieved in His heart.

7   And the LORD said, 'I will blot out man whom I have created from the face of the land, from man to animals to creeping things and to birds of the sky; for I am sorry that I have made them.'

8   But Noah found favor in the eyes of the LORD.

Make a big box around verse 9. Do you remember that this is a key phrase in the Book of Genesis?

9   These are the records of the generations of Noah. Noah was a righteous man, blameless in his time; Noah walked with God.

10 And Noah became the father of three sons: Shem, Ham, and Japheth.

Circle three more important people found in verse 10.

Do you see another key word in verses 11 and following? Mark it throughout the chapter (and choose the symbol you want to use).

11 Now the earth was corrupt in the sight of God, and the earth was filled with violence.

12 And God looked on the earth, and behold, it was corrupt; for all flesh had corrupted their way upon the earth.

13 Then God said to Noah, 'The end of all flesh has come before Me; for the earth is filled with violence because of them; and behold, I am about to destroy them with the earth.

Another key word begins in verse 14. Decide the symbol you will use and mark it everywhere it appears in the chapter.

14   Make for yourself an ark of gopher wood; you shall make

the ark with rooms, and shall cover it inside and out with

pitch.

15   And this is how you shall make it: the length of the ark

three hundred cubits, its breadth fifty cubits, and its

height thirty cubits.

16   You shall make a window for the ark, and finish it to a

cubit from the top; and set the door of the ark in the side

of it; you shall make it with lower, second, and third decks.

17   And behold, I, even I am bringing the flood of water upon

the earth, to destroy all flesh in which is the breath of life,

from under heaven; everything that is on the earth shall

perish.

The word 'covenant' is a key word in the Book of Genesis, even though it is only mentioned once here. Make a red square around it and fill it with yellow.

18   But I will establish My covenant with you; and you shall

enter the ark—you and your sons and your wife, and your

sons' wives with you.

19   And of every living thing of all flesh, you shall bring two of

every kind into the ark, to keep them alive with you; they

shall be male and female.

20 Of the birds after their kind, and of the animals after their

kind, of every creeping thing of the ground after its kind,

two of every kind shall come to you to keep them alive.

21 And as for you, take for yourself some of all food which is

edible, and gather it to yourself; and it shall be for food for

you and for them.'

22 Thus Noah did; according to all that God had commanded

him, so he did.

Theme of Genesis 6

Circle the best theme:

    A. God tells Noah that He is going to send a Flood.

    B. Mankind is very evil.

    C. The Ark is described.

Draw a picture of the theme you chose for Genesis 6.

Observation Sheet: Genesis 7

Mark the *who's*: God and Noah. Use the same symbols you have throughout Genesis.

Remember, 'ark' is also a key word. Mark it as you did in chapter 6.

1 Then the LORD said to Noah, 'Enter the ark, you and all your household; for you alone I have seen to be righteous before Me in this time.

2 'You shall take with you of every clean animal seven pairs [by sevens], a male and his female; and of the animals that are not clean two, a male and his female;

3 also of the birds of the sky, seven pairs [by sevens], male and female, to keep offspring alive on the face of all the earth.

There is a WHEN in verse 4. Make a little clock here and everywhere else you see a time reference in the chapter. For example, there is another WHEN in verses 6, 10 and 11. You will have lots of clocks in this chapter!

4 'For after seven more days, I will send rain on the earth forty days and forty nights; and I will blot out from the face of the land every living thing that I have made.'

5 And Noah did according to all that the LORD had commanded him.

6 Now Noah was six hundred years old when the flood of water came upon the earth.

7   Then Noah and his sons and his wife and his sons' wives with him entered the ark because of the water of the flood.

8   Of clean animals and animals that are not clean and birds and everything that creeps on the ground,

9   there went into the ark to Noah two by two [by twos], male and female, as God had commanded Noah.

10 And it came about after the seven days, that the water of the flood came upon the earth.

Verses 11–12 contain the best statement we have of what actually happened in the Flood. Put a big colored box around this verse so that you will be able to find it easily later.

11 In the six hundredth year of Noah's life, in the second month, on the seventeenth day of the month, on the same day all the fountains of the great deep burst open, and the floodgates of the sky were opened.

12 And the rain fell upon the earth for forty days and forty nights.

13 On the very same day Noah and Shem and Ham and Japheth, the sons of Noah, and Noah's wife and the three wives of his sons with them, entered the ark,

Do you see a repeated phrase in verse 14 that you saw in Genesis 1? Highlight or underline it in blue.

14 they and every beast after its kind, and all the cattle after their kind, and every creeping thing that creeps on the earth after its kind, and every bird after its kind, all sorts of birds.

15 So they went into the ark to Noah, two by two of all flesh in which was the breath of life.

16 And those that entered, male and female of all flesh, entered as God had commanded him; and the LORD closed it behind him.

17 Then the flood came upon the earth for forty days; and the water increased and lifted up the ark, so that it rose above the earth.

18 And the water prevailed and increased greatly upon the earth; and the ark floated on the surface of the water.

19 And the water prevailed more and more upon the earth, so that all the high mountains everywhere under the heavens were covered.

20 The water prevailed fifteen cubits higher, and the mountains were covered.

21 And all flesh that moved on the earth perished, birds and

cattle and beasts and every swarming thing that swarms

upon the earth, and all mankind;

22 of all that was on the dry land, all in whose nostrils was the

breath of the spirit of life, died.

23 Thus He blotted out every living thing that was upon the

face of the land, from man to animals to creeping things

and to birds of the sky, and they were blotted out from

the earth; and only Noah was left together with those that

were with him in the ark.

24 And the water prevailed upon the earth one hundred and fifty

days.

Theme of Genesis 7

Circle the best theme:

    A. God closes the door of the Ark.

    B. All the high mountains were covered.

    C. The Flood

Draw a picture of the theme you chose for Genesis 7.

Observation Sheet: Genesis 8

God and Noah are still your *who*'s in this chapter. Mark them throughout the chapter just as you did in previous chapters.

You also have a lot of time indicators in this chapter. Draw a clock over the phrase or in the margin for every WHEN you see.

1 But God remembered Noah and all the beasts and all the cattle that were with him in the ark, and God caused a wind to pass over the earth, and the water subsided.

2 Also the fountains of the deep and the floodgates of the sky were closed, and the rain from the sky was restrained;

3 and the water receded steadily from the earth, and at the end of one hundred and fifty days the water decreased.

In verse 4 you have an important WHERE. Underline or highlight it in green.

4 And in the seventh month, on the seventeenth day of the month, the ark rested upon the mountains of Ararat.

5 And the water decreased steadily until the tenth month; in the tenth month, on the first day of the month, the tops of the mountains became visible.

6 Then it came about at the end of forty days, that Noah opened the window of the ark which he had made;

7 and he sent out a raven, and it flew here and there until the water was dried up from the earth.

You may wish to mark 'dove' as a key word in these verses.

8 Then he sent out a dove from him, to see if the water was abated from the face of the land;

9 but the dove found no resting place for the sole of her foot, so she returned to him into the ark; for the water was on the surface of all the earth. Then he put out his hand and took her, and brought her into the ark to himself.

10 So he waited yet another seven days; and again he sent out the dove from the ark.

11 And the dove came to him toward evening; and behold, in her beak was a freshly picked olive leaf. So Noah knew that the water was abated from the earth.

12 Then he waited yet another seven days, and sent out the dove; but she did not return to him again.

13 Now it came about in the six hundred and first year, in the first month, on the first of the month, the water was dried up from the earth. Then Noah removed the covering of the ark, and looked, and behold, the surface of the ground was dried up.

14 And in the second month, on the twenty-seventh day of the month, the earth was dry.

15 Then God spoke to Noah, saying,

16 'Go out of the ark, you and your wife and your sons and your sons' wives with you.

17 Bring out with you every living thing of all flesh that is with you, birds and animals and every creeping thing that creeps on the earth, that they may breed abundantly on the earth, and be fruitful and multiply on the earth.'

18 So Noah went out, and his sons and his wife and his sons' wives with him.

19 Every beast, every creeping thing, and every bird, everything that moves on the earth, went out by their families from the ark.

20 Then Noah built an altar to the LORD, and took of every clean animal and of every clean bird and offered burnt offerings on the altar.

21 And the LORD smelled the soothing aroma; and the LORD said to Himself, 'I will never again curse the ground on account of man, for the intent of man's heart is evil from his youth; and I will never again destroy every living thing, as I have done.

22 'While the earth remains, seedtime and harvest, and cold and heat, and summer and winter, and day and night shall not cease.'

Theme of Genesis 8

Circle the best theme:

      A. God promises the seasons.

      B. The Flood ends.

      C. God sends a wind to dry up the waters.

Draw below a picture of the theme you chose for Genesis 8.

Observation Sheet: Genesis 9

Who's to be marked in this chapter include God, Noah and the sons of Noah.

God gives a series of commands to Noah in this section. If you can spot them, highlight those commands or underline them with blue.

1 And God blessed Noah and his sons and said to them, 'Be fruitful and multiply, and fill the earth.

2 And the fear of you and the terror of you shall be on every beast of the earth and on every bird of the sky; with everything that creeps on the ground, and all the fish of the sea; into your hand they are given.

3 Every moving thing that is alive shall be food for you; I give all to you, as I gave the green plant.

4 Only you shall not eat flesh with its life, that is, its blood.

5 And surely I will require your lifeblood; from every beast I will require it. And from every man; from every man's brother I will require the life of man.

6 Whoever sheds man's blood, by man his blood shall be shed, for in the image of God He made man.

7 And as for you, be fruitful and multiply; populate the earth abundantly and multiply in it.'

8 Then God spoke to Noah and to his sons with him, saying,

'Covenant' is a key word. Mark every time it appears in the chapter.

9 'Now behold, I Myself do establish My covenant with you, and with you descendants after you;

10 and with every living creature that is with you, the birds, the cattle, and every beast of the earth with you; of all that comes out of the ark, even every beast of the earth.

11 And I establish My covenant with you; and all flesh shall never again be cut off by the water of the flood, neither shall there again be a flood to destroy the earth.'

12 And God said, 'This is the sign of the covenant which I am making between Me and you and every living creature that is with you, for all successive generations;

13 I set My bow in the cloud, and it shall be for a sign of a covenant between Me and the earth.

14 And it shall come about, when I bring a cloud over the earth, that the bow shall be seen in the cloud,

15 and I will remember My covenant, which is between Me and you and every living creature of all flesh; and never again shall the water become a flood to destroy all flesh.

16 When the bow is in the cloud, then I will look upon it, to remember the everlasting covenant between God and every living creature of all flesh that is on the earth.'

17 And God said to Noah, 'This is the sign of the covenant which I have established between Me and all flesh that is on the earth.'

18 Now the sons of Noah who came out of the ark were Shem and Ham and Japheth; and Ham was the father of Canaan.

19 These three were the sons of Noah; and from these the whole earth was populated.

20 Then Noah began farming and planted a vineyard.

Verse 20 has a time word in it. Make a clock over the WHEN.

21 And he drank of the wine and became drunk and uncovered himself inside his tent.

22 And Ham, the father of Canaan, saw the nakedness of his father and told his two brothers outside.

23 But Shem and Japheth took a garment and laid it upon both their shoulders and walked backward and covered the nakedness of their father; and their faces were turned away so that they did not see their father's nakedness.

24 When Noah awoke from his wine, he knew what his

youngest son had done to him.

25 So he said, 'Cursed be Canaan; a servant of servants he

shall be to his brothers.'

There are some more *when*'s in these closing verses. Draw some clocks

26 He also said, 'Blessed be the LORD, the God of Shem; and

let Canaan be his servant.

27 May God enlarge Japheth, and let him dwell in the tents of

Shem; and let Canaan be his servant.

28 And Noah lived three hundred and fifty years after the

flood.

29 So all the days of Noah were nine hundred and fifty years,

and he died.

Theme of Genesis 9

Circle the best theme:

        A. God makes a covenant with Noah.

        B. God promises the seasons.

        C. Noah plants a vineyard.

Draw a picture of the theme you chose for Genesis 9.

Observation Sheet: Genesis 10

We keep seeing this repeated key phrase in Genesis. Draw a big box around it.

Whew, there are so many *who*'s in chapter 10. Just circle (in different colors) wherever you see the phrase 'sons of Japeth,' 'sons of Ham' and 'sons of Shem.'

1 Now these are the records of the generations of Shem, Ham, and Japheth, the sons of Noah; and sons were born to them after the flood.

2 The sons of Japheth were Gomer and Magog and Madai and Java and Tubal and Meshech and Tiras.

3 And the sons of Gomer were Ashkenaz and Riphath and Togarmah.

4 And the sons of Javan were Elishah and Tarshish, Kittim and Dodanim.

5 From these the coastlands of the nations were separated into their lands, every one according to his language, according to their families, into their nations.

6 And the sons of Ham were Cush and Mizraim and Put and Canaan.

7 And the sons of Cush were Seba and Havilah and Sabtah and Raamah and Sabtexa; and the sons of Raamah were Sheba and Dedan.

8   Now Cush became the father of Nimrod; he became a mighty one on the earth.

9   He was a mighty hunter before the LORD; therefore it is said, 'Like Nimrod a mighty hunter before the LORD.'

10   And the beginning of his kingdom was Babel and Erech and Accad and Calneh, in the land of Shinar.

11   From that land he went forth into Assyria, and built Nineveh and Rehoboth-Ir and Calah,

12   and Resen between Nineveh and Calah; that is the great city.

13   And Mizraim became the father of Ludin and Anamim and Lehabim and Naphtuhim

14   and Pathrusim and Casluhim (from which came the Philistines) and Caphtorim.

15   And Canaan became the father of Sidon, his first-born, and Heth

16   and the Jebusite and the Amorite and the Girgashite

17   and the Hivite and the Arkite and the Sinite

18 and the Arvadite and the Zemarite and the Hamathite; and afterward the families of the Canaanite were spread abroad.

19 And the territory of the Canaanite extended from Sidon as you go toward Gerar, as far as Gaza; as you go toward Sodom and Gomorrah and Admah and Zeboiim, as far as Lasha.

20 These are the sons of Ham, according to their families, according to their languages, by their lands, by their nations.

21 And also to Shem, the father of all the children of Eber, and the older brother of Japheth, children were born.

22 The sons of Shem were Elam and Asshur and Arpachshad and Lud and Aram.

23 And the sons of Aram were Uz and Hul and Gether and Mash.

24 And Arpachshad became the father of Shelah; and Shelah became the father of Eber.

25 And two sons were born to Eber; the name of the one was Peleg, for in his days the earth was divided; and his

brother's name was Joktan.

26 And Joktan became the father of Almodad and Sheleph and Hazarmaveth and Jerah

27 and Hadoram and Uzal and Diklah

28 and Obal and Abimael and Sheba

29 and Ophir and Havilah and Jobab; all these were the sons of Joktan.

30 Now their settlement extended from Mesha as you go toward Sephar; the hill country of the east.

31 These are the sons of Shem, according to their families, according to their languages, by their lands, according to their nations.

32 These are the families of the sons of Noah, according to their genealogies, by their nations; and out of these the nations were separated on the earth after the flood.

Theme of Genesis 10

Circle the best theme:

A. Nimrod the hunter

B. The Canaanites and Jebusites

C. The descendants of Noah and the formation of nations

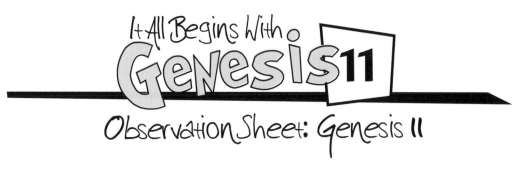

Observation Sheet: Genesis 11

There is an important WHERE mentioned in verse 2. Underline or highlight it in green.

1 Now the whole earth used the same language and the same words.

2 And it came about as they journeyed east, that they found a plain in the land of Shinar and settled there.

'They' and 'us' refer to the people. Circle all these repeated words.

3 And they said to one another, 'Come let us make bricks and burn them thoroughly.' And they used brick for stone, and they used tar for mortar.

4 And they said, 'Come let us build for ourselves a city, and a tower whose top will reach into heaven, and let us make for ourselves a name; lest we be scattered abroad over the face of the whole earth.'

The LORD is always a key word. Mark Him as you have been doing throughout Genesis.

5 And the LORD came down to see the city and the tower which the sons of men had built.

6 And the LORD said, 'Behold they are one people, and they all have the same language. And this is what they began to do, and now nothing which they purpose to do will be impossible for them.

263

7 'Come; let us go down and there confuse their language, that they may not understand one another's speech.'

8 So the LORD scattered them abroad from there over the face of the whole earth; and they stopped building the city.

Here is another WHERE to mark in green.

9 Therefore its name was called Babel, because there the LORD confused the language of the whole earth; and from there the LORD scattered them abroad over the face of the whole earth.

10 These are the records of the generations of Shem. Shem was one hundred years old, and became the father of Arpachshad two years after the flood;

11 and Shem lived five hundred years after he became the father of Arpachshad, and he had other sons and daughters.

12 And Arpachshad lived thirty-five years and became the father of Shelah;

13 and Arpachshad lived four hundred and three years after he became the father of Shelah, and he had other sons and daughters.

14   And Shelah lived thirty years and became the father of Eber;

15   and Shelah lived four hundred and three years after he became the father of Eber, and he had other sons and daughters.

16   And Eber lived thirty four years, and became the father of Peleg;

17   and Eber lived four hundred and thirty years after he became the father of Peleg, and he had other sons and daughters.

18   And Peleg lived thirty years, and became the father of Reu;

19   and Peleg lived two hundred and nine years after he became the father of Reu, and he had other sons and daughters.

20   And Reu lived thirty two years, and became the father of Serug;

21   and Reu lived two hundred and seven years after he became the father of Serug, and he had other sons and daughters.

22 And Serug lived thirty years, and became the father of Nahor;

23 and Serug lived two hundred years after he became the father of Nahor, and he had other sons and daughters.

24 And Nahor lived twenty-nine years, and became the father of Terah;

25 and Nahor lived one hundred and nineteen years after he became the father of Terah, and he had other sons and daughters.

26 And Terah lived seventy years, and became the father of Abram, Nahor and Haran.

Here is that key phrase in Genesis again. Box it in as you have done before.

27 Now these are the records of the generations of Terah. Terah became the father of Abram, Nahor and Haran; and Haran became the father of Lot.

28 And Haran died in the presence of his father Terah in the land of his birth, in Ur of the Chaldeans.

29 And Abram and Nahor took wives for themselves. The name of Abram's wife was Sarai; and the name of Nahor's wife was Milcah, the daughter of Haran, the father of Milcah and Iscah.

30 And Sarai was barren; she had no child.

31 And Terah took Abram his son, and Lot the son of Haran,

his grandson, and Sarai his daughter-in-law, his son

Abram's wife; and they went out together from Ur of the

Chaldeans in order to enter the land of Canaan; and they

went as far as Haran, and settled there.

32 And the days of Terah were two hundred and five years;

and Terah died in Haran.

11

Theme of Genesis 11

Circle the best theme:

    A. The Tower of Babel

    B. All speak the same language.

    C. Abram is born.

Draw a picture of chapter 11.